A NEW DIRECTION

A Cognitive-Behavioral Treatment Curriculum

SHORT-TERM
WORKBOOK

Relapse Prevention

Mapping a Life
of Recovery & Freedom
for Chemically Dependent
Criminal Offenders

**A Collaboration of Chemical Dependency Professionals from
the Minnesota Department of Corrections and the Hazelden Foundation**

HAZELDEN®

Hazelden
Center City, Minnesota 55012-0176

1-800-328-9000
1-651-213-4590 (Fax)
www.hazelden.org

ISBN: 1-56838-859-4

Cover design by David Spohn
Interior design by Terri Kinne
Illustrations by Patrice Barton

Hazelden Publishing and Educational Services is a division of the Hazelden Foundation, a not-for-profit organization. Since 1949, Hazelden has been a leader in promoting the dignity and treatment of people afflicted with the disease of chemical dependency.

The mission of the foundation is to improve the quality of life for individuals, families, and communities by providing a national continuum of information, education, and recovery services that are widely accessible; to advance the field through research and training; and to improve our quality and effectiveness through continuous improvement and innovation.

Stemming from that, the mission of this division is to provide quality information and support to people wherever they may be in their personal journey—from education and early intervention, through treatment and recovery, to personal and spiritual growth.

The headquarters of the Hazelden Foundation are in Center City, Minnesota. Additional treatment facilities are located in Chicago, Illinois; New York, New York; Plymouth, Minnesota; St. Paul, Minnesota; and West Palm Beach, Florida. At these sites, we provide a continuum of care for men and women of all ages. Our Plymouth facility is designed specifically for youth and families.

For more information on Hazelden, please call **1-800-257-7800.** Or you may access our World Wide Web site on the Internet at **www.hazelden.org.**

CONTENTS

A NEW DIRECTION

A Cognitive-Behavioral Treatment Curriculum

Acknowledgments

Thanks to all who have contributed to this curriculum:

Sheryl Ramstad Hvass
Commissioner, Minnesota Department of Corrections

Peter Bell
Executive Vice President, Hazelden Publishing and Educational Services

James D. Kaul, Ph.D.
Director, TRIAD Chemical Dependency Program
Minnesota Department of Corrections

Will Alexander
Sex Offender/Chemical Dependency Services Unit, Minnesota Department of Corrections

Minnesota Department of Corrections

Sex Offender Treatment Program at Lino Lakes Minnesota Correctional Facility

Robin Goldman, Director
Jim Berg, Program Supervisor
Brian Heinsohn, Corrections Program Therapist
Greg Kraft, Corrections Program Therapist
K. Kaprice Borowski Krebsbach, Corrections Program Therapist
Kevin Nelson, Corrections Program Therapist
Tim Schrupp, Corrections Program Therapist
Pamela Stanchfield, Corrections Program Therapist
Jason Terwey, Corrections Program Therapist
John Vieno, Corrections Program Therapist
Cynthia Woodward, Corrections Program Therapist

TRIAD Chemical Dependency Program at Lino Lakes Minnesota Correctional Facility

Launie Zaffke, Supervisor
Randy Tenge, Supervisor
Carmen Ihlenfeldt, Acting Supervisor
Thomas A. Berner, Corrections Program Therapist
Toni Brezina, Corrections Program Therapist
Jeanie Cooke, Corrections Program Therapist
Ronald J. DeGidio, Corrections Program Therapist
Susan DeGidio, Corrections Program Therapist
Maryann Edgerley, Corrections Program Therapist
Connie Garritsen, Corrections Program Therapist
Gerald Gibcke, Corrections Program Therapist
Anthony Hoheisel, Corrections Program Therapist
Deidra Jones, Corrections Program Therapist
Beth Matchey, Corrections Program Therapist
Jack McGee, Corrections Program Therapist
Jackie Michaelson, Corrections Program Therapist

Hal Palmer, Corrections Program Therapist
Terrance Peach, Corrections Program Therapist
Holly Petersen, Corrections Program Therapist
Linda Rose, Corrections Program Therapist
Kathy Thompson, Corrections Program Therapist
Beverly Welo, Corrections Program Therapist

Reshape Chemical Dependency Program at Saint Cloud Minnesota Correctional Facility

Robert L. Jungbauer, Director
Christine Fortson, Corrections Program Therapist
Tracanne Nelson, Corrections Program Therapist
Jeffrey D. Spies, Corrections Program Therapist

Atlantis Chemical Dependency Program at Stillwater Minnesota Correctional Facility

Bob Reed, Director
Dennis Abitz, Corrections Program Therapist
Bill Burgin, Corrections Program Therapist
Tom Shipp, Corrections Program Therapist

New Dimensions Chemical Dependency Program at Faribault Minnesota Correctional Facility

Michael Coleman, Supervisor
Michele Caron, Corrections Program Therapist

Central Office

Jim Linehan, Corrections Program Therapist

Minnesota Department of Corrections Supervising Agents

Russ Stricker, Correctional Unit Supervisor
Bobbi Chevaliar-Jones, Intensive Supervised Release Agent
William Hafner, Corrections Agent
Gregory Fletcher, 180 Degrees Halfway House

In Addition:

Writers: Corrine Casanova, Deborah Johnson, Stephen Lehman, Joseph M. Moriarity, Paul Schersten. **Designer:** Terri Kinne. **Typesetters:** Terri Kinne, Julie Szamocki. **Illustrator:** Patrice Barton. **Prepress:** Don Freeman, Kathryn Kjorlien, Rachelle Kuehl, Joan Seim, Tracy Snyder, David Spohn. **Editor:** Corrine Casanova. **Copy editors:** Monica Dwyer Abress, Kristal Leebrick, Caryn Pernu. **Proofreaders:** Catherine Broberg, Kristal Leebrick. **Marketer:** Michelle Samlaska. **Video production manager:** Alexis Scott.

Special thanks: Any Color Painting Company; Blue Moon Production Company; Eden Re-entry Services; inmates and staff of Lino Lakes, Rush City, and Stillwater Minnesota Correctional Facilities.

Special thanks to Hazelden: Nancy Alliegro, Derrick Crim, Joe Fittipaldi, Carole Kilpela, Nick Motu, Karin Nord, Patricia Owen, Rebecca Post, Teri Ryan, Ann Standing, Sue Thill, and Kris VanHoof-Haines.

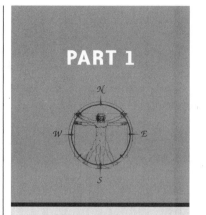

Getting Started

You've been straight and off alcohol and other drugs for a while. You're probably feeling better physically than you have in quite a long time. You might be starting to feel better about yourself, too. And you should. It's a big deal not to use alcohol and other drugs. It's not easy.

Making permanent life changes takes more than a little promise to yourself. Even though it is difficult, many alcoholics and addicts *have* quit using for good. It *is* possible to leave crime, alcohol, and other drugs behind.

This workbook is about learning how to keep the changes you've made going—and living a life free of crime, alcohol, and other drugs.

One of the major problems in recovery from alcohol and other drug use is relapse—a return to drinking or using after a period of not using. Relapse could happen with you. Recovery from alcohol and other drug use—and from a criminal lifestyle—is an ongoing process. To succeed, you must quit using alcohol and other drugs. You must stop your criminal behaviors. And you must develop new, positive thinking patterns, attitudes, and behaviors.

There is a very strong connection between your criminal behavior and your alcohol and other drug use. If you relapse into drinking and using, criminal activity is likely to follow. The opposite is also true: if you get involved with criminal activities, it's very likely that you'll begin drinking or using again.

In this workbook, you'll learn more about

- what a relapse is
- identifying situations that put you at high risk for relapse
- taking steps to avoid those high-risk situations before you relapse
- making a relapse prevention plan that will reduce your chances of relapse
- building a support network that can help you stay sober and away from crime
- what to do if you relapse

"It's your best thinking that got you here."

— Anonymous

The Consequences of Your Choices

Before you start working on your relapse prevention plan, remind yourself just why you are trying to stop committing crimes and using alcohol and other drugs. Remembering this will help you focus on the work ahead.

Just How "Good" Were the "Good Old Days"?

Think about the last crime you committed and were convicted of. Now answer the following questions.

➤ What was the crime?

_____

_____

➤ What did you think was going to happen to you as a result of committing this crime? (For example, you thought all your problems would go away once you got the money.)

_____

_____

➤ What actually happened?

_____

_____

_____

➤ What role did drugs play in this crime? For example, did you get high so you could do the crime, or did you commit the crime for money to buy drugs?

_____

_____

_____

➤ Who were the victims of your crime?

_____

_____

_____

➤ How were those victims hurt by it? What were the consequences for them?

_____

_____

_____

Who were the victims of your crime?

➤ How do you think each of your victim(s) felt or still feels about this event?

_____

_____

_____

➤ What effect did your crime have on the following people:

Your spouse or partner?

_____

_____

Your children (if you have kids)?

_____

_____

Your parents or grandparents?

_____

_____

➤ How much time did you get for this crime?

_____

_____

"One of the most important things that I have gotten out of AA is not to be ashamed to ask for help. When someone has a gun pointed at you, you are scared. That's how I feel about my drug habit. Drugs have a gun pointed at me, and it's ready to fire. I'm scared, because I know that if I make that wrong move, the gun will go off. That's the problem I'll face when I get out. AA has taught me that being scared is smart."

— Lester T.,
   aggravated burglary, 10 years,
   Jester Unit I, Texas
   (Free at Last)

"You can map out a fight plan or a life plan, but when the action starts it may not go the way you planned, and you're down to your reflexes—which means your training. That's where your roadwork shows. If you cheated on that in the dark of the morning—well, you're getting found out now, under the bright lights."

— Joe Frazier, heavyweight boxing champion from 1970 to 1973,
   best known for his three classic bouts with Muhammad Ali

➤ Next, think of two times when you got high and then ended up in trouble. What happened to you because of your alcohol or other drug use?

_____

_____

_____

Who else was affected by your using?

_____

_____

_____

How was each person listed above affected?

_____

_____

_____

■

When you were drinking or using and committing crimes, maybe you saw only the "benefits" of these activities but not the consequences. Let's take a closer look at that kind of thinking.

The Positives and Negatives
of Drinking or Using

➤ List the "benefits" or "positives" of drinking or using as
you saw or still see them.

_____

_____

➤ Next, list the "negatives."

_____

_____

The Positives and Negatives
of Crime

➤ List the "benefits" or "positives" of crime as you saw or still
see them.

_____

_____

➤ Next, list the "negatives" of crime.

_____

_____

*Your higher power
makes your life
uncomfortable
when it's time for
you to change.*

Look again at the "positives" you listed for drinking or using and crime. Chances are you listed power, freedom, money, and fun. At first it seemed exciting. But it was all short-lived. And now, in the end, you have no power, no freedom, and little fun in your life—because drug use and crime eventually led you behind bars. And that's *exactly* what will happen again once you are out—unless you are serious about leaving crime and alcohol and other drugs behind.

You might be thinking, "I know what I did wrong last time. Next time, I won't get caught." But eventually, you will get caught. You've told yourself that before. You'll land back behind bars. You can bank on it. How many times have you heard a fellow inmate say something like, "Man, when I get out, I ain't never coming back"? He probably really meant it when he said it. But by not changing his drinking/drug use and criminal behavior, he ended up behind bars again.

How can you have freedom, power, money, and respect? By starting to live free of crime, alcohol, and other drugs. This may be hard to believe, but it's true. And it's the only choice you have. You tried the other path, and where did it lead? Right to where you are now.

Your best chance to make your dream of getting out and *staying out* come true is through treatment and recovery. The cold, hard truth is that if you can't beat your addiction, you'll likely die behind bars—or at a young age on the streets.

Remember Why You're Here and How You Got Here

Once you've served your time, you can't just walk out the door and expect everything to be great. Success in recovery and in life on the outside takes a good plan and hard work. By doing the work in this workbook, you will create your own relapse prevention plan that works just for you. Then, it's up to you to follow it.

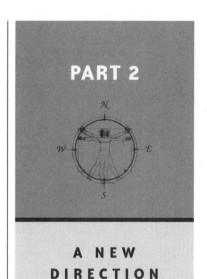
Understanding the Relapse Process

Relapse is the process of returning to the use of alcohol or other drugs after a time of quitting. Relapse is always possible. It doesn't matter how long you have been sober. In this workbook, you will learn about the relapse process. You will create a recovery plan to help you prevent relapse.

Think of what you did to pursue alcohol and other drugs.

Now, go after NOT drinking or using with the same energy and determination.

Many alcoholics and drug addicts who have relapsed know that there were many clues to relapse long before it happened.

Relapse warning signs involve your behavior, attitudes, feelings, thoughts, or a combination of all of these.

Lapse vs. Relapse

A *lapse* happens when you are very close to drinking, using drugs, or getting involved in criminal activity but haven't actually "crossed the line." A lapse happens when you put yourself in a situation where you've used before and would be tempted to use again.

A *relapse* happens when you actually use alcohol or other drugs or take part in a criminal activity.

Relapse clues or lapses include:

Changes in your behavior

- not attending meetings regularly
- isolating yourself from people who are helping you stay sober
- hanging out with friends who are selling drugs even though you're not
- contacting former using buddies
- contacting former sexual partners who use, even if you're telling yourself that you're doing it to get them to quit
- cutting back on support group meetings

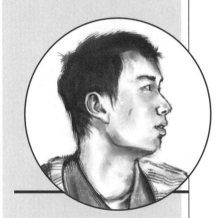

Changes in your behaviors, attitudes, feelings, and thoughts could mean that your relapse process has already started.

Changes in your attitude

- not caring about sobriety
- thinking you can quit drinking or using so you can commit crimes and not get caught
- getting cocky with recovery
- not caring about what's happening in your life
- becoming too negative about how your life is going

Changes in your feelings or mood

- increased moodiness or depression
- strong feelings of anger at yourself or others
- increased feelings of boredom
- telling "war stories" with fellow inmates
- looking to find faults in others as excuses to use
- sudden feelings of euphoria

Changes in your thoughts

- thinking you "deserve" to use alcohol or drugs because you've been sober for several months
- thinking you don't need to attend meetings because you're "better" now
- thinking it wouldn't hurt to use just once
- thinking your alcohol and other drug problems are "cured" because you haven't used for some weeks or months

Of course, you won't relate to all these examples. The important thing to remember is that changes in your behaviors, attitudes, feelings, and thoughts could mean that your relapse process has already started.

A relapse happens when you actually use alcohol or other drugs or take part in a criminal activity.

Making big changes is not like flipping a light switch—as in, "I did things this way yesterday," and now (flipping the switch), "I'll do those things differently today." In a way, relapse is a normal part of the change process.

BUT: There's a big, big difference between a relapse for someone like you and relapse for alcoholics who have never been incarcerated. If they relapse, they might miss a day of work or their kid's softball game. Chances are, they won't end up incarcerated for relapsing—and *you* could.

Your situation is very different. You are an addict *and* a criminal with a record. When you relapse and start using again, you will hurt, victimize, or kill someone—or yourself. Once you get started, you can't control yourself. You damage or destroy everyone you touch. You'll be right back where you are now, but with even more time to serve.

That's why it's so important to pay attention to your thoughts. Watch for signs of criminal and addictive thinking. That's when you have to recognize your lapses—*before* you've actually done something that violates your parole, that hurts someone, or that is illegal.

There is a great danger of relapse during this early stage of recovery. As you know, recovery takes more time, energy, and emotional involvement than you first thought. We are giving you information and exercises to help you recognize when *you* are in danger of a relapse, and we are explaining some ways to prevent it. These are long-term changes that can help you live a life free of drinking, using, and criminal behaviors.

What Leads Up to a Relapse?

First, let's look more closely at what leads up to a relapse. Addicts see relapses as impulsive—a moment of weakness when they let down their guard. This is not true. Stress, coping strategies (or lack of them), and decision-making skills all play a role, as do SUDs—seemingly unimportant decisions. Relapse is really the *final* result of a chain of events that starts days, weeks, or even months before it happens. The relapse cycle in figure 1 shows how this works.

Figure 1
CRIMINAL BEHAVIOR AND ALCOHOL-OTHER DRUGS RELAPSE CYCLE

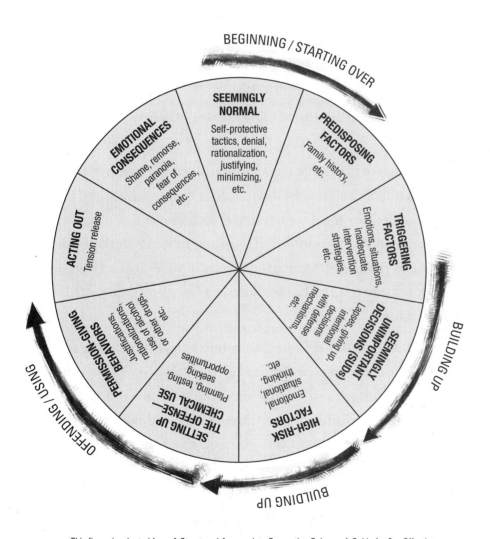

This figure is adapted from *A Structured Approach to Preventing Relapse: A Guide for Sex Offenders*, by Robert E. Freeman-Longo and William D. Pithers (Brandon Vt.: Safer Society Press, 1992).

Often, the actual relapse doesn't happen right away because the time isn't right. Instead, you relapse in your mind through secret planning or fantasies. You then rationalize them away or deny having done this, or both.

Addictive substances make permanent changes in your brain chemistry. That's why recovery requires total abstinence from any drug, not only the one you first became addicted to.

These two distorted ways of thinking come together to create a chain of events leading to a relapse. People who are headed for a relapse make a number of seemingly unimportant decisions (SUDs), each moving them a bit closer to relapse. A recovering alcoholic who buys a twelve-pack of beer to take home, "just in case guests drop by," is making a SUD.

When you "set up" a relapse like this, it gives you an excuse to avoid responsibility for the relapse. By putting yourself in high-risk situations, you can say you were "overwhelmed" and it was "impossible" to resist relapse. The reality is that *you* put yourself in this position.

You are <u>always</u> the one responsible for your behavior.

Identifying and Stopping Your Criminal Behavior Cycle

You are both an addict and a criminal. Because of this, you need to build a relapse prevention plan for both your criminal and addictive behaviors. To stay crime-free, you need to understand your own criminal behavior cycle. Once you do, you will know when you're going into it. That's the time to stop it and move in a positive direction.

Your Criminal Cycle

This exercise will help you understand your criminal cycle.

➤ What are the specific acts and other behaviors that generally made up your offenses?

_____

_____

_____

_____

➤ What places did you look for or cruise for victims? Where and when were you "doing the work"?

_____

_____

_____

_____

➤ In what places did you set up your victims?

_____

_____

➤ Where did you commit your criminal activity?

_____

_____

➤ At what times of the day were you most likely to commit crimes?

_____

_____

➤ In what times of the year were you most likely to commit crimes?

_____

_____

■

By identifying your criminal behavior and alcohol-other drugs relapse cycle in figure 1 (page 13), you'll be able to intervene *before* you act out or relapse again. You don't need to hit rock bottom first.

Figure 1 will help you to understand your personal criminal behavior and drinking-using cycle. Now you will know *where* and *how* you can prevent acting out and relapse.

An addict/alcoholic is a sick human being trying to get well, not a bad person trying to be good.

There is hope even if you do act out or relapse. There is no need to give up and go on a binge or crime spree. Chances are you will have lapses. Be prepared for them. When it happens, know that it is okay and safe to talk about them with the right people. Go to someone who is supporting you in recovery. Talk to your sponsor, group, religious leader, counselor, or your supervising agent. Ask one or more of these people to help you make a better plan for working out your problems. Don't give up! Don't fall back into negative thinking! Reoffending or using will lead you back on the road to incarceration and death.

EXERCISE 4 EXERCISE

Observable Behaviors

➤ To disrupt your cycle, you need to know when you are slipping into criminal behavior or drinking and using behaviors. (Review your answers in exercise 3, Your Criminal Cycle.) In the space below, write the behaviors other people will see when you are getting into your cycle.

_____

_____

_____

_____

_____

Share this information with your support group. They will then be able to confront your behaviors. This will help you get out of your cycle without reoffending or using.

Effects of Your Criminal Cycle on Your Life

➤ Look at the two columns below. For each topic listed, use the left-hand column to write about how these areas of your life are affected when you are in your cycle. In the right-hand column, describe how these areas of your life look when you are *not* in your cycle.

	Life in the criminal cycle	Life when not in the criminal cycle
Financial	_____	_____
	_____	_____
	_____	_____
	_____	_____
Support groups	_____	_____
	_____	_____
	_____	_____
	_____	_____
Employment and education	_____	_____
	_____	_____
	_____	_____
	_____	_____

	Life in the criminal cycle	Life when not in the criminal cycle
Appearance	_____ _____ _____ _____	_____ _____ _____ _____
Social interactions	_____ _____ _____ _____	_____ _____ _____ _____
Appetite	_____ _____ _____ _____	_____ _____ _____ _____
Sleep patterns	_____ _____ _____ _____	_____ _____ _____ _____

continued on next page

19

	Life in the criminal cycle	Life when not in the criminal cycle
Use of alcohol or other drugs	_____ _____ _____ _____	_____ _____ _____ _____
Leisure activities	_____ _____ _____ _____	_____ _____ _____ _____
Driving	_____ _____ _____ _____	_____ _____ _____ _____
Marriage or relationship with partner	_____ _____ _____	_____ _____ _____

Negative Self-Talk and Positive Self-Talk

Much of your criminal behavior cycle happens in your mind. Thoughts, fantasies, and talking negatively to yourself are high-risk factors for reoffending and relapsing. Don't let them run free in your head. Put a stop to it now.

Here are some examples of negative self-talk:

"Nobody likes me." "I'm a failure. I can't do anything right." "Nothing I do is good enough."

➤ In the space below, write the negative self-talk that is part of your criminal cycle.

_____

_____

_____

_____

➤ Next, write the positive self-talk that you can use to challenge your negative thinking. For example,

"I have a sponsor who cares about me," or "I'm working hard to make healthy changes."

_____

_____

_____

_____

It's now time to do something to be proud of.

Replacing negative thoughts with positive ones is important. Throughout this workbook, we will be asking you to give up negative behaviors. Remember that each negative behavior should be replaced with a positive behavior. We'll help you do this, too.

When You're Not Feeling Good about Yourself

Recovering from addiction and a criminal lifestyle isn't easy. And we know that it *is* easy to get down on yourself. Let's be honest—you have done some things worth regretting. But that's in the past.

It's now time to do something to be proud of—take positive steps. When you're feeling down on yourself, it's time to intervene. It's time to take the following action:

1. Call a support person.

2. Think about something positive you've done.

3. Admit to yourself that you're not feeling good about yourself.

4. Say something positive about yourself to yourself.

5. Look in a mirror and say, "I'm okay. I like myself."

6. Try to find good in everything; use your mistakes to help someone else.

7. Write to someone.

8. Do not dwell on the past. (Decide what positive action you can take now to move your recovery ahead.)

9. Dress neatly.

10. Talk with someone about how you're feeling.

11. Look at the facts clearly.

12. Read a good book.

13. Make plans to do something safe that you'll feel good about doing.

14. Play a sport.

15. Give yourself a compliment.
    (See the list of affirmations in exercise 7.)

16. Don't assume anything.

17. Deal with situations in ways you're proud of.

18. Change "I can't" to "I can."

19. Accept that you don't have to be perfect.

20. Do something that shows achievement.

21. Deal with problems in a positive way.

22. Find something to do that you like.

23. Live as if it's the last day of your life.

24. Eliminate negative statements about yourself.

25. Write about your feelings in your journal.

26. Remind yourself that you're okay, not perfect,
    and that's all right.

27. Spend time with sober friends.

28. Talk with someone from your treatment team.

29. Remind yourself that you're in a better place than
    some people. (Count your blessings.)

30. Think about positive things you've done.

31. Stop stalling and do what you need to do.

32. Look at how you've improved.

33. Get some exercise.

34. Get help from AA or NA groups and a sponsor.

35. Think about your feelings and why you feel this way.

36. Be sensitive to others.

37. Do something kind for someone.

Using Positive Affirmations

What are affirmations? They are positive statements that you use to change the way you see yourself and the world around you. Think of them as positive self-talk. As the saying goes, "Thinking makes it so." You have used negative self-talk for years. It's not enough just to stop. You need to replace your negative thoughts with positive self-talk. Tell yourself that hard work pays off, and it will. Tell yourself that you're a healthy, positive person, and eventually you'll believe you are. Repeating affirmations to yourself may seem silly or stupid, but it isn't. It can change lives. Professional athletes use them all the time to improve performance.

Here are some affirmations that can help you in your recovery:

1. I can have a craving without acting on it.
2. I am learning to disagree without being disagreeable.
3. I have positive goals I want to accomplish.
4. I am always doing the best that I can.
5. I am very capable of changing my own behavior that I don't like.
6. I can stay in control of myself as long as I am relaxed.
7. I don't have to be perfect at everything.
8. I can stay sober.
9. I don't have to act on my anger.
10. Progress, not perfection.
11. I give myself credit for the little things I accomplish each day.

12. I am fully able to change.

13. Fear of pain can be more uncomfortable than the pain itself.

14. Looking back, I can see how far I've come.

15. When I don't get what I want, I may get something even better.

16. The name of the game is service to others.

17. Nothing is so awful that I can't handle it.

18. The strength I seek from the outside can only come from within me.

19. I am strong enough to be kind and gentle.

20. When I forgive others, I forgive myself.

21. I am responsible for my own feelings and actions.

22. I can be strong enough to risk failure and rejection.

23. I am part of a powerful network.

24. My mistakes can teach me what not to do.

➤ Write down several of your own affirmations that will help you stay out of your criminal cycle.

_____

_____

_____

_____

_____

"I don't fight anymore and I don't try to control others. I simply believe that with the help of a higher power, I am changed. I'm working this recovery program because it's helping me to remember that I'm striving for a better future and a new outlook on life. Since I've been in treatment, a lot of my old ways of thinking have toned down or gone away. In group now, I can actually talk out my problems. I asked for help because I want to live a life of sobriety and let go of my old self."

— Frank S.,
   possession and sale of a
   controlled substance, 25 years,
   St. Clair Correctional Facility,
   Alabama
   (Free at Last)

Deterrents to Drinking, Using and Reoffending

The following five deterrents will help prevent you from drinking, using drugs, and reoffending.

Deterrent 1:
Stop! Think of immediate consequences.

Deterrent 2:
Stop and think: Who gets hurt?

Deterrent 3:
Plan ahead, think ahead, and make another choice.

Deterrent 4:
Examine your conscience and take a daily moral inventory.

Deterrent 5:
Do not dwell on it.

EXERCISE **8** EXERCISE

Deterring Use

➤ Describe a recent situation that put you at risk.

_____

➤ How would you act differently if you were in the same situation again and used the deterrents listed above?

_____

_____

_____

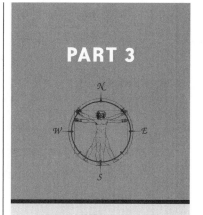

PART 3

Triggers, Cravings, and High-Risk Situations

Triggers, cravings, and high-risk situations can push people who are close to relapsing into criminal activity or drinking/using behaviors.

Not everyone's urges, cravings, triggers, and risk factors are the same, but everyone has them. Your chances of relapsing are greater if you are in the early stages of recovery. That's because you haven't deactivated the triggers in your life.

A big and very important part of relapse prevention is identifying your **triggers** and **cravings,** or **urges.** You can't avoid or stop them unless you recognize them first. Your job now is to do just that—figure out what people, places, situations, objects, beliefs, emotions, attitudes, and reactions will put you at high risk for relapsing. Think about these for both inside your correctional facility and outside in the world. In this section, we'll help you do that. If a condition of your treatment plan or probation requires you to avoid certain people, places, and situations, avoid them! You shouldn't even question this—unless you are prepared to once again give up your freedom.

Trigger

A *trigger* is something outside of you that puts you at risk for relapse. Triggers are people, places, situations, or objects.

Urge or Craving

An *urge,* or *craving,* comes from inside you. It's a belief, emotion, attitude, or a reaction to a situation that puts you at risk for relapse.

 EXERCISE 9 EXERCISE

Identifying Your Triggers and Cravings

➤ What people, places, situations, objects, beliefs, emotions, attitudes, and reactions will put you at high risk for relapsing in your correctional facility?

_____   _____

_____   _____

_____   _____

_____   _____

_____   _____

➤ What people, places, situations, objects, beliefs, emotions, attitudes, and reactions will put you at high risk for relapsing in the outside world?

_____   _____

_____   _____

_____   _____

_____   _____

_____   _____

_____   _____

➤ In your own words, why is it important to know your risk factors?

_____

_____

_____

_____

There is a difference between the urge to use and a compulsion to use. Most recovering people, even after many years, continue to have using thoughts and using dreams. The difference is that they know what to do to keep that urge from becoming a compulsion.

EXERCISE 10 EXERCISE

Your Most Recent Drinking or Using Episode

A return to drinking or using is most likely to happen if you return to the same situations, places, and people involved in your most recent use. By examining your most recent use, you will be able to see what situations, places, and people put you at risk for relapse.

➤ List all mood-altering chemicals you used during your last three months of use.

_____

_____

_____

_____

➤ List the people involved in your drinking or using during the last three months of your use. If necessary, complete this exercise in a notebook.

Who did you drink or use with?

_____

_____

Who did you buy from?

_____

_____

➤ Who did you avoid?

_____

_____

➤ List all the places you drank or used during your last three months of using. If necessary, complete this exercise in a notebook.

_____

_____

_____

_____

_____

_____

It's not the size of the step that matters, just that you take it.

➤ Do you believe that mood-altering chemicals might still be stashed in your home, garage, workplace, or vehicle? (check one)

_____ Yes   _____ No

Recovery isn't a death sentence;

it's a life sentence.

Relapse Trigger Checklist

Here are eight relapse triggers:

1. thoughts, feelings, attitudes, or behaviors

2. social pressures to use alcohol or other drugs

3. problems related to your sobriety plan or treatment plan

4. problems in relationships with other people

5. urges, cravings, temptations, or testing "control"

6. triggers related to relapse-oriented or addictive personality traits

7. triggers related to your physical, emotional, and mental health

8. miscellaneous other triggers

We'll take a closer look at these triggers in the following pages. Once you identify your relapse triggers in each group, we will help you plan relapse prevention strategies. This will help you cope without using alcohol or other drugs—and without reoffending.

Thoughts, Feelings, Attitudes, or Behaviors

You have had a lot of practice holding negative thoughts in your mind. You have rehearsed acts of confrontation, revenge, hate, and violence. And at times, you have acted on those thoughts. Feelings like hate, confusion, anger, fear, and loneliness can lead you back to incarceration or can even lead to death.

As we said, relapse is a process. You must remain aware of the process. Relapse results when you begin to play with thoughts or behaviors that support your old ways of living.

It's not necessary to deny these thoughts and feelings. Instead, pay more attention to them. They are signs that something's wrong—that you are getting closer to a relapse. Since you are responsible for your recovery, when you notice these thoughts, take action. What should you do? The following exercises offer action steps.

The NBA and Your Relapse Prevention Plan

You may think you don't need a relapse prevention plan, but you do. Here's why. Think about a professional basketball team in the National Basketball Association (NBA). Players spend hours practicing set plays to use in critical situations. When there's ten seconds left in a close game, they know it's not the time to try a new play. They want to have the set down cold so they know exactly what to do.

Relapse prevention plans serve the same purpose, except that a lot more is at stake—you! If the Lakers, Knicks, or 76ers lose the game, the team still gets to come back for the next game. If you "lose" and relapse, you're back behind bars, playing ball in the yard. You don't want to suddenly find yourself in a potential relapse situation without a plan. You want to be ready. You want to have a plan down solid so you know exactly what to do. That plan starts now with thinking about situations that you know could trigger a relapse for you.

Your Triggers Related to Thoughts, Feelings, Attitudes, or Behaviors

Triggers Related to Negative Emotional States

It's easier to enjoy life as a sober person in recovery. But life in recovery does not guarantee happiness forever! In the beginning, there's a lot of hard stuff to get through—including negative emotional states.

➤ Place an **X** in the box next to the triggers that apply to you.

____ anger expression problems (for example, holding anger in or expressing anger inappropriately, such as with violence)

____ anxiety or nervousness

____ acting out violently or destructively

____ boredom or lack of constructive leisure interests

____ denial (saying, "I don't have an alcohol or drug problem anymore")

____ becoming depressed

____ excessive or impulsive behaviors (for example, gambling, overeating, spending too much money, overworking, excessive sex)

____ fears about staying sober

____ feeling helpless or hopeless

____ feeling guilty

____ impatience with your recovery plan (for example, thinking that things are happening too slowly)

____ lack of meaning in life (nothing seems important)

____ loneliness or isolating yourself from others

____ overconfidence about sobriety (for example, "I've got this thing licked" or "I'll *never* use alcohol or drugs again")

____ painful memories (for example, the death of a loved one, growing up in a troubled family, combat experience)

____ preoccupation with alcohol or other drugs

____ resentment toward others

____ self-pity

____ shame

____ thinking alcohol or other drugs are needed in order to have fun

____ unusual or disturbing thoughts

____ other (write in): _____

Triggers Related to Positive Emotional States

Some recovering alcoholics and addicts don't have too much trouble dealing with the negatives. Instead, the relapse happens when they're feeling better and life is going well.

➤ Place an **X** next to triggers that you can relate to.

____ thinking of using as a reward

____ thinking, "My problems are behind me"

____ using as a part of celebrations (holidays, birthday parties, and so on)

____ cycles of feeling intense emotional highs

____ other (write in): _____

Example:

Shaun's Story

Shaun is twenty-nine, married, with one child. He did time for drug possession and has been out of prison for a year and a half. He is an alcoholic and has used pot a lot, too. Shaun was in treatment while in prison. He has relapsed once. At the time of his relapse, he had been sober for about ten months. That's when he started thinking that he had his problem licked. This was about the time friends started telling him how good he looked and how well he seemed to be doing. He also started telling himself that smoking pot would be okay if he limited his use and that he didn't need NA meetings because "things were under control."

Shaun's Relapse Warning Signs:

1. thinking that he has the problem licked

2. thinking that he's doing great and no longer needs meetings

3. thinking that he can control his pot use

Shaun's Relapse Prevention Plan:

1. discuss his thoughts about smoking pot immediately with his wife and sponsor

2. try to identify why his denial returned

3. change his thoughts from "I have this licked" to "I cannot safely smoke pot."

4. write down all the reasons why he should not smoke pot or use alcohol

5. deliberately avoid people he smoked pot with

6. return to NA meetings

Review the items you marked on pages 34 and 35. Circle the two that are most "dangerous" for you. Review the facts related to each relapse trigger and fill in the information in the space provided. If necessary, complete this exercise in a notebook.

▶ **First relapse warning sign:**

_____

Relapse prevention plan:

1. _____

_____

2. _____

_____

3. _____

_____

4. _____

_____

5. _____

_____

➤ **Second relapse warning sign:**

_____

Relapse prevention plan:

1. _____

   _____

2. _____

   _____

3. _____

   _____

4. _____

   _____

5. _____

   _____

Sometimes, the relapse happens when you're feeling better and life is going well.

Social Pressures to Use Alcohol or Other Drugs

To stay sober, you have to learn to deal successfully with social pressures. These pressures may be direct (being offered drugs or a drink) or indirect (being involved in a family gathering or work-related event where alcohol or other drugs are being used).

Remember: when you are in these situations, you will be uncomfortable. For example, you might feel

- nervous and worried because your sobriety is being threatened
- angry that others can drink or use and you can't
- disconnected from your old group of friends or co-workers
- sorry for yourself that you can't drink or use
- like telling yourself "one or two won't hurt"

In early recovery, you can avoid many social situations that pressure you to use alcohol or other drugs. Do this by planning your day-to-day activities around events and places where alcohol and drugs are not available. Stay away from bars and parties where alcohol and other drugs will be used.

It's impossible to avoid all social pressures to drink or use. Recovering addicts and alcoholic deal with this by

- saying straight out that they have a problem with alcohol or other drugs
- simply refusing without giving an explanation
- saying that they are not using today
- offering an alternative activity (for example, if they want to spend time with a person who wants to go to a bar to drink, they say, "I'm not drinking. Let's go someplace for coffee instead")

If you begin to feel more and more pressure in a social situation, just leave, if possible.

Some Places Mean Trouble

Remember that relapse is a process. Dangerous places can get the process going. What kind of places should you avoid? Common sense and your relapse prevention plan will guide you.

Avoid bars, old connections, and parties where alcohol and other drugs will be used, and other places that might be dangerous for you.

If you have problems with gambling, avoid bookies, the races, casinos, pull tabs, online betting, bingo parlors, and even the lottery.

If you have problems with sexual misconduct, you will need to stay away from sexually oriented magazines, adult bookstores, the Internet, theaters, and strip clubs.

EXERCISE **12** EXERCISE

Places to Stay Away from to Avoid Relapse

List all the people and places you need to avoid to prevent relapse.

▶ People I need to avoid:

_____

_____

_____

_____

When you feel needy, get up and give.

➤ Places I need to avoid:

_____

_____

_____

_____

_____

➤ Talk with your group, counselor, supervising agent, clergy, tribal elder, and others to help you decide what other places and people put you at high risk for relapse.

■

Alan's story . . .

I was twenty-eight when I was mandated into a rehab program because of problems with alcohol and other drugs like pot, Quaaludes, Preludin, and cocaine. About a month after I finished the program, four of my old friends stopped over to see me. After a few minutes, one of them suggested that we all go to a local club and have a few beers. Although I wanted to go, I knew this wasn't a good idea for me. So I said, "I'm not drinking," and suggested they stay at my place and watch the ballgame on TV. Things seemed to be going okay, but after about a half hour, one of my friends broke out some coke and said, "Hey, let's get high!" I was really uncomfortable with this. It took about all the strength I had, but I refused to do any cocaine.

Alan's Relapse Prevention Plan

When Alan talked with his support group later that week, they helped him create this plan.

1. He will decide which friends he can hang out with without having the constant threat of being offered drugs. He will cut ties with several old friends whose relationships with him were based mostly on getting high.

2. He will not go to the local club where he often drank with friends.

3. He will begin to develop relationships with people who do not misuse alcohol or use other drugs.

4. He will become actively involved in social and recreational activities sponsored by NA groups in his area.

5. He will tell other friends that he has an addiction and can't safely use any addictive substance.

6. He will invite a small group of sober friends over to his home each week for activities that don't revolve around getting high.

As Alan's story shows, to stay in recovery, you absolutely need a relapse prevention plan. You need to be aware of difficult situations even before they happen. You need to know how you might be affected by them. Most important, you need to have a plan in place to deal with difficult situations without drinking or using.

Your Triggers Related to Social Pressures

➤ Place an **X** next to the triggers for using alcohol or other drugs that apply to you.

____ events where alcohol or drugs are likely to be used (parties, picnics, family gatherings, concerts, weddings, ballgames, etc.)

____ going to a bar or club

____ being around your old friends who use

____ difficulty refusing alcohol or other drugs when offered by others

____ being around people who are intoxicated or high

____ other (write in): _____

➤ Review the social pressures you marked above. Think about how they will affect both your thoughts and your feelings. In the space provided, write down three possible social pressures and the thoughts and feelings you might have when they happen.

Social pressure #1: _____

Your thoughts: _____

_____

_____

Your feelings: _____

_____

_____

Social pressure #2: _____

Your thoughts: _____

_____

_____

Your feelings: _____

_____

_____

Social pressure #3: _____

Your thoughts: _____

_____

_____

Your feelings: _____

_____

_____

Review the facts related to each of these situations, and
then write your relapse prevention plan. To help you get
started, you might want to review Alan's story and his
relapse prevention plan on pages 40–41.

➤ **First relapse warning sign:**

_____

Relapse prevention plan:

1. _____

   _____

2. _____

   _____

3. _____

   _____

4. _____

   _____

5. _____

   _____

➤ **Second relapse warning sign:**

_____

Relapse prevention plan:

1. _____

   _____

2. _____

   _____

3. _____

   _____

4. _____

   _____

5. _____

   _____

Problems Related to Your Sobriety Plan or Treatment Plan

As a recovering addict or alcoholic, you need to participate in a support group of some kind. There's a difference, however, between "going to group" and "using your group." If you are hiding information and forcing the group members to work to get through to you, then you're just "going to group." "Using your group" means that you let down your guard. You allow others to know who you really are. This includes sharing when you're in trouble, taking chances, trusting the group, and asking for help.

Many people have found great support for recovery through attending AA or NA meetings. You have a choice. You can go to meetings and just sit in a corner. Or you can go to meetings, listen, introduce yourself, talk with people, tell your story—your whole story. Make a contribution at each meeting. When you find a group that works for you, make a commitment to it. Remember, you're trying to build a support network. Meetings are a great place to start. These people will understand you because they have been where you are now. They know firsthand how to help and support you. After all, they were helped and supported by those who came before them.

You have to work your program. This means really participating in a recovery program. It involves a strong commitment to your recovery program. Your program may be different from a Twelve Step program with different assignments and goals. But that's really not important. You could go to any program and still find help as long as you are committed to it. The best program in the world can't help you if you aren't committed to it. Commitment is the key to success. You truly need to *work* your program.

The best program in the world can't help you if you aren't committed to it.

Problems in Relationships with Other People

Many people like you have relapsed and reoffended by hanging out with people they thought of as friends. The risks of doing this may seem simple and obvious now, but they often aren't at the time. Even if you just want to check up on your old running partners, there is no guarantee that they won't put you in danger. Develop strength in your recovery program *before* putting yourself in dangerous situations. If these people are true friends, they will support you and be willing to meet you in places where you won't be at risk. Keep yourself in situations where you have control. If someone you know insists on meeting you in a place that will put you at risk, he or she is not really a friend.

 **EXERCISE 14 EXERCISE**

Relationships with Others

Circle either **T** for true or **F** for false for each of the following statements.

1. **T** **F** I can control myself in high-risk situations.

2. **T** **F** I can be around anybody I want if I don't engage in criminal or high-risk behavior, even if they do.

3. **T** **F** I can still "be down with the fellas" and work a recovery program as long as I don't get caught up in the game.

4. **T** **F** My crime partners, homies, and other friends write me and visit me regularly.

5. **T** **F** My crime partners, homies, and other friends have supported me while I have been down.

6. **T** **F**   It is best to hang out with other people in recovery if I want to remain free.

7. **T** **F**   Even if I am trying to do the right thing, I cannot control high-risk or criminal situations.

8. **T** **F**   Twelve Step programs such as AA and NA are good places to meet people for friendship and support in recovery.

9. **T** **F**   It is best to avoid old crime partners and connections altogether.

➤ The following are possible triggers from your relationship with your spouse or partner. Place an **X** next to triggers that apply to you.

____ a spouse or partner who is not willing to participate in treatment to support recovery

____ a spouse or partner who is abusive (physically, emotionally, sexually, or verbally)

____ anger management problems, including abuse, in the relationship

____ problems with trust and resentment in the relationship

____ a spouse or partner who has an alcohol or other drug problem

____ the possibility of separation or divorce

____ sexual problems

____ problems with parents, other relatives, or in-laws

____ problems related to being a parent

➤ Here are other triggers that have to do with relationships. Place an **X** next to those that apply to you.

_____ arguing with others

_____ difficulty meeting people or developing new relationships

_____ difficulty trusting others

_____ having no friends, being a loner

_____ being friends mainly with people who abuse alcohol or other drugs

_____ having friends who don't support your sobriety

_____ not knowing how to make friends without using

_____ other (write in): _____

Review the items you marked. Choose two relapse warning signs that you are most concerned about right now. Review the facts related to each one, and then write your relapse prevention plan.

➤ **First relapse warning sign:**

_____

Relapse prevention plan:

1. _____

_____

2. _____

_____

3. _____

_____

4. _____

_____

5. _____

_____

➤ **Second relapse warning sign:**

_____

Relapse prevention plan:

1. _____

_____

2. _____

_____

3. _____

_____

4. _____

_____

5. _____

_____

Should You Stay in Your Relationship?

If you have a spouse or partner and want to stay in the relationship, you need to ask yourself some questions. First, is this person an alcoholic or addict? If so, staying in the relationship won't work unless your spouse or partner begins treatment.

Even if your spouse or partner does not have a problem with drugs or alcohol, returning to the relationship the way it was before will still put your recovery at great risk. Recovery is more important than any relationship. What good is it if the two of you stay together and you relapse? You'll end up back behind bars. This person will be gone from your life either way.

If you want to try to save the relationship, both of you will need professional counseling.

Urges, Cravings, Temptations, or Testing "Control"

During recovery, particularly the early months, urges or cravings to use alcohol or other drugs are common. An urge or craving can occur at any time, even if you are in a recovery program. Urges and cravings can differ for each person in how often and in how intense they are.

Urges and cravings can be triggered by anything that reminds you of drinking or using. Being nervous or angry can also be triggers. Physical signs include a tightness in your stomach or feeling nervous throughout your body.

Thinking signals are when you begin having more and more thoughts about how much better you could feel by using or drinking. You might also start thinking that you "need" a drink or other drugs.

Urges and cravings can be triggered by anything that reminds you of drinking or using.

Triggers for Urges, Cravings, and Temptations

Think about the last time you had an urge or craving for alcohol or another drug.

➤ What triggered your urge or craving?

_____

_____

_____

➤ What did your body do (the physical signs)?

_____

_____

_____

➤ What were you thinking (the psychological signs)?

_____

_____

_____

Paying Attention to Your Urges and Cravings

This exercise is an ongoing assignment. You'll need a notebook to continue this exercise. Whenever you have an urge or craving for alcohol or other drugs, write down exactly what you were doing and thinking when this happened. Next, write down all the reasons why you should *not* get high again. Do this *every time* you have an urge or craving to get high.

It's time to learn more about what brings on your urges or cravings. The four questions below will help you deal with them in a positive way. As you know, the temptations, pressures, and opportunities to use will be even stronger once you are out. For now, answer the questions as they relate to your last urge or craving.

➤ Write down the answers to these four questions in your notebook. Do this **every time** you have an urge or craving.

1. What triggered your urge or craving?

2. What did your body do (the physical signs)?

3. What were you thinking (the psychological signs)?

4. Why should I get drunk or high?

Whenever you think about using, remember the worst situation that alcohol or other drugs ever put you in.

Positive, Effective Ways to Handle Urges and Cravings

In the early stages of recovery, you're not prepared to deal with urges and cravings. But it is possible to learn how to handle them successfully. Many recovering alcoholics and addicts are able to survive urges or cravings to use or drink. Here are some ideas for how to do this:

1. **Talk with others.**
   Talk with someone—either in person or on the phone—such as a sober and healthy friend or family member, your sponsor, a minister, tribal elder, priest, or rabbi. Attend AA, NA, or other support group meetings. Ask for a counseling appointment. Keep a list of the names and phone numbers of sober people who will be there for you at all times.

2. **Redirect your activity.** Read a book or magazine. Write your thoughts and feelings in a journal. Get something to eat. Pray. These activities may take your mind off your urge or craving. Physical activities can also help you relax.

3. **Change your thoughts.**

   • Tell yourself that you will put off using alcohol or other drugs until tomorrow.

   • Think of all the bad things that have happened to you because of your drinking or using.

   • Whenever you think about using, remember the worst situation that alcohol or other drugs ever put you in. This is probably what will happen if you drink or use again. The negative experience is the reality.

   • Think of how good you will feel if you do not use.

   • Think of all the benefits of being sober, both now and in the future. Make a list of these benefits in your notebook, if necessary.

- Think positively: "I'm not going to use" or "I will get through this urge or craving without using."

- Repeat some of the recovery slogans, such as "One day at a time" or "Easy does it" or "This, too, will pass."

4. **Avoid threatening situations.**

   After you're released from incarceration, don't go to bars, parties, or clubs where you think it will be even more difficult to handle your urge or craving. Avoid socializing with others who want you to use or drink.

 EXERCISE 17 EXERCISE

Relapse Prevention Plans
for Urges and Cravings

Write down an urge or craving and how you will cope with it. Ask your counselor and group members to help you.

➤ **Relapse warning sign:**

_____

Relapse prevention plan:

1. _____

2. _____

3. _____

4. _____

5. _____

Here's some good news: remember that urges and cravings happen less and less—and they're less powerful—the longer you are in recovery and sober.

Relapse will happen if you . . .

1. ignore your urges
2. live on the edge
3. don't have anything to do
4. don't carry any phone numbers for people in your support network
5. don't have a goal
6. think only of yourself
7. don't eat or sleep properly
8. don't use your recovery tools when you need them
9. don't plan ahead
10. feel sorry for yourself, blame others, hang on to resentment
11. don't care
12. lie
13. think of using drugs and doing crime as fun

Triggers Related to Relapse-Oriented or Addictive Personality Traits

Exercise 18 explores potential triggers related to addictive and criminal thinking patterns.

 EXERCISE 18 EXERCISE

Relapse-Oriented or Addictive Personality Traits

➤ Place an **X** next to the triggers that apply to you.

____ thinking that you are your own worst enemy

____ problems getting motivated

____ being negative or sarcastic a lot

____ problems trusting others

____ resenting and "blame collecting"

____ holding grudges

____ problems with authority

____ needing to be "different"

____ being impulsive (acting without thinking)

____ needing excitement

____ being hyperactive: can't slow down, always need to be doing something

____ needing to be accepted by others, no matter what

____ other (write in): _____

Review the items you marked. Choose two that you are most concerned about right now. Review the facts related to each one, and then write your relapse prevention plan.

➤ **First relapse warning sign:**

_____

Relapse prevention plan:

1. _____

_____

2. _____

_____

3. _____

_____

4. _____

_____

5. _____

_____

➤ **Second relapse warning sign:**

_____

Relapse prevention plan:

1. _____

   _____

2. _____

   _____

3. _____

   _____

4. _____

   _____

5. _____

   _____

Triggers Related to Physical, Emotional, and Mental Health

Exercise 19 explores potential triggers related to physical, emotional, and mental health.

EXERCISE **19** EXERCISE

Triggers Related to Physical, Emotional, and Mental Health

Place an **X** next to the triggers that apply to you.

➤ *Physical Health*

____ chronic physical problems such as back pain, diabetes, and so on

____ unhealthy lifestyle—poor eating habits, poor nutrition, no exercise, being overweight

____ always being tired

____ sleep problems—too much, not enough, regular dreams about using

____ an injury or ailment (or dental work) that requires a mood-altering chemical such as painkillers, muscle relaxants, and so on

➤ *Emotional Health*

____ mood swings

____ continued feelings of depression or anxiety

____ guilt about your use and previous relapses

____ history of mental or emotional health problems

➤ *Mental Health*

___ history of long-term regular use of alcohol or other drugs

___ recent heavy use of alcohol or other drugs

___ workplace environment that has solvents, inks, dyes, or paint fumes

___ problems with short-term memory or making decisions

Review the items you marked. Choose two that you are most concerned about right now. Review the facts related to each one, and then write your relapse prevention plan.

➤ **First relapse warning sign:**

_____

Relapse prevention plan:

1. _____

   _____

2. _____

   _____

3. _____

   _____

4. _____

   _____

61

5. _____

_____

➤ **Second relapse warning sign:**

_____

Relapse prevention plan:

1. _____

_____

2. _____

_____

3. _____

_____

4. _____

_____

5. _____

_____

*Relapse will happen
if you feel sorry
for yourself, blame
others, or hang
on to resentment.*

Miscellaneous Other Triggers

Exercise 20 explores other potential triggers that may cause relapse. Beware of those relapse triggers that happen when it appears as if your life is starting to turn around.

 EXERCISE 20 EXERCISE

Miscellaneous Triggers

➤ Place an **X** next to the triggers that apply to you.

____ success at your job (for example, getting promoted)

____ high-stress lifestyle (long work hours, pressure, etc.)

____ family history of chemical dependency

____ difficulty handling evenings or weekends

____ difficulty handling stress or anxiety

____ family history of abuse (sexual, physical, emotional, or verbal)

____ difficulty solving problems without getting over-whelmed

____ feeling good and happy about yourself and your life

____ lack of hobbies or leisure-time interests

____ physical pain or problems

____ wanting to celebrate special occasions (holidays, birthdays, etc.)

____ other (write in): _____

Review the items you marked. Choose two that you are most concerned about right now. Review the facts related to each one, and then write your relapse prevention plan.

➤ **First relapse warning sign:**

_____

Relapse prevention plan:

1. _____

   _____

2. _____

   _____

3. _____

   _____

4. _____

   _____

5. _____

   _____

➤ **Second relapse warning sign:**

_____

Relapse prevention plan:

1. _____

   _____

2. _____

   _____

3. _____

   _____

4. _____

   _____

5. _____

   _____

Taking Action

Much of this relapse prevention material is designed to help you once you've been released. Don't wait until you are on the outside to take action on preventing relapse. Now is the time to start. Correctional facilities are not always free of alcohol and other drugs. Relapse can, and does, happen inside. Start practicing now during your incarceration. While you're still incarcerated, you have the support of your group leader or counselor and group. The more controlled environment behind bars will also keep you from some of the temptations you'll face after release. Take this time to strengthen your relapse program.

Daily Disciplines

➤ 1. List the actions you will take each day—your daily disciplines—to strengthen your recovery and avoid relapse.

_____

_____

_____

➤ 2. Identify one action you will take during the next seven days on your relapse prevention plan.

_____

➤ 3. After presenting this plan to your group and getting their comments, list below any concerns or suggestions given.

_____

_____

_____

_____

_____

■

Your recovery depends on developing a consistent and effective relapse prevention plan. In the coming weeks, you will add to your plan and change it to make it even better.

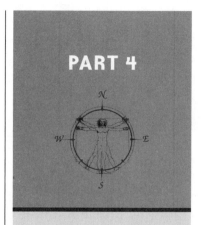

Forms of Support

You're in a hard spot. You're starting to think about your life. Maybe some of your peers who've been in treatment for a while are pressing you to be more honest with yourself. Maybe you're beginning to doubt the way you've seen yourself. You might also question whether you really need so much help in dealing with your criminal and addictive behaviors.

Just remember, you can't do this alone!

Finding a Trustworthy Person Who Can Help You

First, you need to accept that you have a problem and that you haven't been able to beat it on your own. Addiction to alcohol and other drugs has nothing to do with willpower. It's an illness—and you need the help of others to recover from it.

Trust us. You can't make these changes on your own. We have seen many, many people try to do that—and then fail. Needing help from someone doesn't mean you're weak. We all need help sometimes. It's okay to admit that. A good *sponsor* will help you commit to change.

Having a good sponsor makes all the difference in staying free from drugs and crime. Without a good sponsor, you lessen your chances of success no matter how much you want it or how hard you work. Remember, you can't do this alone!

Sponsor

A *sponsor* is a clean, sober person who is active in a recovery program. This will be the person you can turn to in a crisis or call at any time. This person will give you a kick in the pants when you are making excuses and offer hope when you are thinking about giving up on recovery.

Choosing a Sponsor

Choosing a sponsor is a very important decision. You will tell this person the details of crimes you've committed, along with information on alcohol and other drug use. Your sponsor must be a person you can really trust. This person must also be committed to you. Your sponsor must be someone you respect and listen to even if he says something you don't want to hear.

When you choose your sponsor, don't choose your girlfriend, partner, any relative, or someone you might be sexually attracted to. These people are too close to you and your problems.

A sponsor must

- be clean and sober for at least a year or more

- be of the same gender

- believe that abstinence is the only solution for addicts

- be objective and supportive

- be trustworthy

- be able to help you find solutions for your problem

- be objective and tell you what he thinks, even if you don't want to hear it

- have the above qualities *and* be active in a recovery program

  (Examples of recovery programs are Alcoholics Anonymous, Narcotics Anonymous, Men for Sobriety, 13 Feathers, and Walking the Red Road. See page 145 of the appendix.)

A sponsor must be someone you truly respect, not for how much money he has or the car he drives, but for who he is as a person.

Sponsors have jobs. They have families and care about them and other people. They don't rob and steal or do drugs. They have the respect of their family members, friends, and community because they've earned it. They do things for others. It's how they "give back."

Although you can have more than one sponsor, you need to have one person who will be your primary, or main, sponsor. You will also need other people in your life who can help support your recovery.

While you are still incarcerated, talk with your counselor for advice on who could be your sponsor. This person might be a senior peer in your program. Some recovery programs like AA can get you a sponsor while you are still incarcerated. When you are released, this person may continue to be your sponsor.

Talk to your counselor about different options available to you now.

Choosing a Sponsor

➤ Make a list of the people in your life who could be your sponsor. In the space provided, write the reasons for and against each person being a good sponsor. Consider the qualities each person has, such as being truthful, trustworthy, caring, able to keep secrets. A sponsor should meet the guidelines on page 69 and also have the time to help you. Your sponsor should strongly believe that your only hope is no alcohol and other drug use or criminal activity.

____ Person: _____

Reasons **for** being a good sponsor: _____

_____

_____

Reasons **against** being a good sponsor: _____

_____

_____

____ Person: _____

Reasons **for** being a good sponsor: _____

_____

_____

Reasons **against** being a good sponsor: _____

_____

_____

____ Person: _____

Reasons **for** being a good sponsor: _____

_____

_____

Reasons **against** being a good sponsor: _____

_____

_____

_____ Person: _____

Reasons **for** being a good sponsor: _____

_____

_____

Reasons **against** being a good sponsor: _____

_____

_____

_____ Person: _____

Reasons **for** being a good sponsor: _____

_____

_____

Reasons **against** being a good sponsor: _____

_____

_____

➤ Rank the people on your list from the best to least acceptable choice. (Number one should be the best, number two the second best, and so on.) Place this number on the line next to the person's name.

Talk with your group about each of them. Ask your support group or therapist which person, if any, would work best as your sponsor and why. If none of the people are going to work out, start a new list in your notebook.

Once you choose a sponsor, talk with your group leader about exactly how to start your sponsor relationship with this person. Keep in mind that a sponsor is there for you, but on one condition: you must share everything—even your very worst secrets. It's okay to admit how out of control you have been. Your sponsor isn't there to judge you.

Choosing a Support Group

If you're young, you may think you won't be able to relate to older people involved in a support group or AA-type meeting. In truth, these people can offer you excellent recovery help and wisdom, even if you think you don't have a lot in common. Our advice is to go to some kind of support meeting that has older members. Use this group to get solid recovery help. Also, find another meeting with members closer to your age. You can use this group to find more fellowship. It's possible to get both fellowship and wisdom in one group. But if you can't, don't give up. It's okay to go to two different groups.

You may have to try many meetings or groups before you find one that seems right for you. You should go to a given group four, five, or six times before judging it as good or bad. First impressions aren't always accurate.

Other Sources of Support

New supportive friends can also be found in religious communities of different faiths. Every church, temple, or mosque has members like you who are in recovery and will be glad to help you. Tell your minister, priest, rabbi, or other religious leader your story and ask for help.

You will always need help from other people to stay free of crime, alcohol, and other drugs. That help is available, even while you are behind bars. It's time to act now.

Now you know that the consequences of your criminal behavior and your drinking or using did affect others.

As you move ahead, try not to be too discouraged. Many people have stayed in recovery by doing the work outlined in this workbook. Finding and regularly seeing a therapist, if you can do this after your release, can help you in many ways. Often, addictive and criminal behaviors are symptoms of deeper, unresolved, long-term problems. These might include depression or issues from childhood and family life. Dealing with depression or anxiety requires professional help. Medications prescribed by a doctor might also help with these problems.

You may ask why you really need so much help in dealing with these behaviors. Again, accept that you have a problem. If you'd been able to handle alcohol and other drugs on your own, you wouldn't be incarcerated and in this program. Depression, anxiety, and addiction, for example, have nothing to do with willpower or how strong a person you are. You need more help to work through these problems.

Combined therapies are important, too. Don't focus on only one source of help, such as a Twelve Step group, group therapy, or seeing a therapist. Getting help in more than one way increases the chances of your success.

Who Do You Respect? And Why?

Your criminal lifestyle made you loyal to your friends and your drinking/using buddies. But think for a moment. Who do you really look up to? Who are your positive role models? Who do you really respect for who they are as people? Is your role model a gang leader, addict, or drug dealer? Probably not. Who are these people you respect and what do they do? They probably have jobs and don't drink or use. Maybe it's your grandmother, a social worker you know, someone who runs the local community center, or a teacher you had in school.

These are people who are making a difference in other people's lives. They have the respect of their families and friends and people in their community. They've earned this respect because of who they are as people—because of what they do for others and their community. They probably live in the same environment you came from, but they are making different choices in their lives. They would tell you that they like who they are and are happy with life. Is that something you can say about you and your life right now? The good news is that you can change. With time, hard work, and courage, you can be that kind of person.

In your criminal life, you have been loyal and responsible. Those are excellent and important qualities to have. But you need to use them differently. They *can* be used in a different setting.

Stop worrying about what certain people are going to think about you and the changes you're making. Until now, your whole focus has been on how other people saw you. You're always looking for approval from other people. You're worried about your image. Forget that and start thinking about what your children or parents will think of you. What about what *you* think of yourself and your life?

Who Is a Positive Role Model for You?

Think of a person in your life you really look up to. This is someone who is a positive role model, someone you respect for who he or she is as a person. If necessary, complete this exercise in a notebook.

➤ Person's name _____

➤ Who is this person? _____

➤ Why do you look up to this person?

_____

_____

_____

➤ Write about how your lives are alike and different.

_____

_____

_____

➤ What choices did this person make to live a life you respect? Is it a life free of crime and drugs?

_____

_____

_____

➤ What choices did you make that got you where you are today? What choices did you make that kept you from having the respect of others like this person has?

_____

_____

 EXERCISE **24** EXERCISE

Your Support People

➤ Who will be the four most supportive people in your life when you first get out from behind bars?

1. _____

2. _____

3. _____

4. _____

➤ What are the four most important things you need to ask them to help you with?

1. _____

2. _____

3. _____

4. _____

Parole and Probation

Many inmates believe that the rules of parole and probation are there just to set them up to get busted. Because of this, they have a negative attitude toward their supervising agent (parole officer). By beginning your relationship with disrespect, dishonesty, and suspicion, you are just setting yourself up for another fall.

Probation and parole can be a positive, supportive experience. It is actually the last leg on your journey to freedom. If you choose, you can make it work for you. It can help you manage your freedom as you try to get your life organized again. Supervising agents can help you stay straight. They can be a resource for you. They know employers who hire ex-felons. They can help you find halfway houses, community services, emergency clothing, or counseling. They don't want to see you relapse or reoffend. Just be willing to work with them and ask for help.

There are parole and probation officers who see their clients as losers. Missed appointments, dirty urine analyses (UAs), and failure to appear in court or over the phone are all parole violations. Don't want to violate your parole? Then, follow directions, stay clean, keep appointments, and work hard. You will then succeed! A power struggle with your supervising agent will only lead to defeating yourself. It doesn't matter what your supervising agent's attitude is toward you. Successfully completing probation and parole depends on the choices you make, and *only* on your choices. Parole or probation is only a temporary condition if you follow the rules.

Expect nothing. Blame no one.

Do something.

Parole and Your Responsibilities

➤ If you miss appointments, have dirty UAs, fail to appear in court, or fail to report over the phone, what will your supervising agent do?

_____

_____

➤ If you get into a power struggle with your supervising agent, who will lose?

_____

_____

➤ Who is responsible for successfully completing your probation and parole?

_____

➤ What will happen if you respect the conditions of your parole or probation?

_____

_____

➤ List a benefit of working with your supervising agent.

_____

Parole and Probation: Plan for Success

Making your parole and probation successful will lead you to long-term freedom. The following five tips will help you plan for success.

1. **Be honest.**

   It is time to show that you are trustworthy, responsible, and willing to work with others. Don't try to fool your supervising agent. Remember, they are used to clients that con, manipulate, and hide facts. There are no new excuses.

2. **Discuss your problems.**

   Don't try to hide troubles, especially if they can lead to a relapse or violation. Discussing problems with your supervising agent shows that you are serious about living free. If you are honest, your supervising agent will probably go the extra mile to help you.

3. **Follow your relapse prevention or treatment plan.**

   Honor all of the conditions of your probation or parole. Attend all counseling sessions and support groups mandated by the courts or your supervising agent. Also check into other support groups that could help you stay sober and crime free. There are Twelve Step groups such as AA, NA, CA (Cocaine Anonymous), or GA (Gamblers Anonymous) and other support groups for almost every issue you might have. These groups also provide key support and friendships that you will need once you are released.

4. **Follow your supervising agent's directions.**

   You must follow the rules set forth by your supervising agent even if you think he or she is not being fair. Probation and parole is not about being right; it is about living free.

Probation and parole is not about being right; it is about living free.

5. **Keep all appointments and commitments.**
   This is a way to develop a greater sense of trust and
   respect. When you fail to report, it looks like you have
   something to hide. Not keeping appointments shows
   that you can't be counted on to follow the most basic
   condition of probation or parole. Show your supervising
   agent that you are responsible and call ahead if you
   will be late or need to change your appointment.

 EXERCISE 26 EXERCISE

Making Your Plan to Complete Parole and Probation Successfully

Complete the following statements using your own words.

➤ 1. I will demonstrate honesty and responsibility with my
   supervising agent by . . .

   _____

   _____

➤ 2. When I have problems and concerns, I will . . .

   _____

   _____

➤ 3. My relapse prevention plan and the conditions of my
   parole or probation are key to my success after I am
   released. I will take the following actions to make it
   successful:

   _____

   _____

➤ 4. Even if I feel that my supervising agent is being unfair,
   I will . . .

   _____

   _____

   _____

➤ 5. Working with my supervising agent is in my best
   interest. I will honor all conditions of my probation by
   taking the following action:

   _____

   _____

   _____

   _____

   _____

➤ 6. After completing parole and probation, I can apply the
   following actions that I listed above to my daily life:

   _____

   _____

   _____

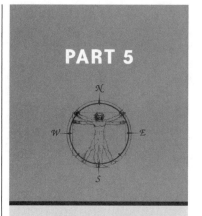

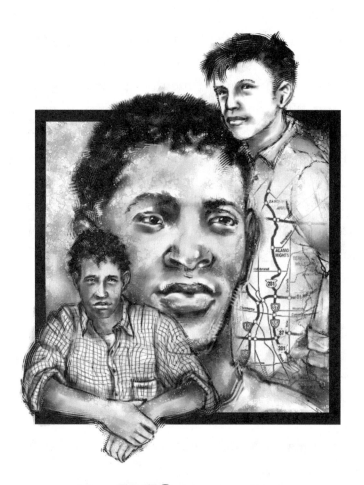

Adding to Your Relapse Prevention Plan

Now it's time to make your relapse prevention plan more complete. It's important that you have your plan all worked out while you're still incarcerated. By starting now, you will be even better prepared for life on the outside.

First, you need to think about your personal recovery goals. This might be difficult. After all, in the past you have focused on what you *don't* want to do—what you are trying to get away from. It's now time to begin working *toward* something. What do you want to see happen in your life? You will have a much better chance of staying free of alcohol, other drugs, and criminal activity if you have clear goals for yourself. Your goals should include simple, fun stuff that you like to do, too. It could be going on a fishing trip, going to a ball game, working out, biking, or Roller-blading regularly. Answering the questions in exercise 27 will help you do this.

EXERCISE 27 EXERCISE

Your Goals in Recovery

Honestly answer the following questions. It will help you on the road to recovery.

➤ What are your plans or goals for your first day outside of incarceration? List your plans or goals on the calendar on page 85.

➤ What are your goals for your first week after your release? List them on the calendar

➤ What are your goals for the first month after you are released? List them on the calendar.

INITIAL RECOVERY GOALS

SUNDAY	MONDAY	TUESDAY	WEDNESDAY	THURSDAY	FRIDAY	SATURDAY

➤ What are your goals for six months after your release?

_____

_____

_____

➤ What are your goals for one year after your release?

_____

_____

_____

➤ What are your goals for two and a half years after your release?

_____

_____

_____

➤ What are your goals for five years after your release?

_____

_____

_____

➤ Identify three personal traits you need to change to help you avoid relapse into addiction or crime. (For example, learning to deal with your anger or changing your thinking that tells you the world owes you whatever you want.)

1. _____

   _____

2. _____

   _____

3. _____

   _____

➤ Identify three major problems you need to fix relating to your work. (For example, learning to accept the authority of a boss or supervisor.)

1. _____

   _____

2. _____

   _____

3. _____

   _____

Happiness is wanting what you have, NOT having what you want.

Sobriety Maintenance Plan

A sobriety plan is the foundation of your recovery plan. You need to know what *you* need to do to keep *you* sober. Remember, sobriety takes skill and a lifelong commitment. It doesn't just happen. Take the specific steps we've given you and practice sobriety skills. By doing so, you will greatly increase your chances of staying sober and living a better life free of crime, alcohol, and other drugs.

 EXERCISE **28** EXERCISE

Your Sobriety Plan

Answer the following questions in the space provided. Then, discuss your answers with your counselor and your group.

Sobriety: Your Commitment to Recovery

➤ What have you learned in this sober time that strengthens your commitment to staying sober?

_____

_____

_____

➤ What benefits have you gained as a result of getting sober?

_____

_____

_____

_____

➤ What risks do you continue to take?

_____

_____

_____

**Sponsor: A Trusted Sober Person Who Has a
Strong Recovery Plan**

➤ Do you have a sponsor? (check one)

_____ Yes   _____ No

If you do not have a sponsor yet, refer to the information
on finding a sponsor in part 4, page 68.

➤ Do you need a sponsor? Why or why not?

_____

_____

➤ Who is your sponsor and how did you meet?

_____

_____

➤ What is the relationship like?

_____

_____

➤ Who contacts who?

_____

_____

➤ Where and how often do you meet?

_____

_____

➤ What happens if there's a problem?

_____

_____

➤ Is the relationship what you expected? (check one)

_____ Yes   _____ No

Why or why not?

_____

_____

➤ Is this a positive relationship for you? (check one)

_____ Yes   _____ No

Why or why not?

_____

_____

➤ In what areas of your recovery will you need help from your sponsor in the future?

_____

_____

➤ Do you think your sponsor can give you that help? (check one)

_____ Yes _____ No

Why or why not?

_____

_____

Daily Recovery Activities

➤ What are your daily recovery-related activities?

_____

_____

_____

_____

➤ What happens if you don't do them?

_____

_____

What are your daily recovery-related activities?

➤ How do you feel when you don't do them daily?

_____

_____

➤ How do these activities help you stay focused on recovery?

_____

_____

➤ How do they help you identify relapse warning signs?

_____

_____

➤ What do you do when you notice a warning sign?

_____

_____

➤ Do you need to change or add anything to your daily disciplines? (check one)

_____ Yes   _____ No

Why or why not?

_____

_____

Other Issues

➤ In the space provided, describe any other steps you can take to help yourself stay sober.

_____

_____

_____

➤ After you complete this sobriety plan, your counselor and group will have a chance to give you their comments and suggestions. List any concerns they raised here and then add them to your plan when time allows.

1. _____

2. _____

3. _____

4. _____

5. _____

6. _____

Your ability to have a lasting recovery depends on your success in making an effective sobriety plan.

"When I was on drugs, I didn't care about myself or how others saw me. All that mattered to me was another hit. And after it was gone, another one after that, and on and on. The program has taught me how self-love plays a role in recovery. I know now that if I love something, I will take care of it. That includes me. Drugs destroy my body. So, I plan to keep a healthy body."

— George S.,
  theft of property, 7 years,
  St. Clair Correctional Facility,
  Alabama
  (Free at Last)

Sobriety Skills

Keeping sober takes skill and a lifelong commitment. It's not just an accident or good luck! It's very important to know some basic sobriety skills. Examples are listed below, but this list is not complete. Work alone—and then with your group—to make this list more complete. Remember, what one person finds easy may be a big problem for someone else.

You will face difficult situations related to drinking or using. What will you do? Here are some examples of risky situations you may need to deal with:

- how to say "no" when someone offers you alcohol or other drugs

- how to handle a call from your dealer

- what to do when you go home and a family member offers you alcohol or another drug

- what to do when your girlfriend stops by your house three days after your release with beer and some cocaine and says, "Let's go over to my place"

- what to do when someone lights up a joint

- what to do if you find a bottle in your closet

- what to do when a couple of friends stop over with a twelve-pack of beer

What to Do When . . .

What situations do you find difficult? These could be situations you shared in group. List them in the space provided and then describe how you will deal with each of them.

➤ Situation:

_____

_____

My reaction:

_____

_____

_____

➤ Situation:

_____

_____

My reaction:

_____

_____

_____

➤ Situation:

_____

_____

My reaction:

_____

_____

_____

➤ Situation:

_____

_____

My reaction:

_____

_____

_____

➤ In your notebook, describe additional risky situations and what your reaction would be.

Making an Emergency Sobriety Card

Many ex-inmates and recovering alcoholics/addicts carry an Emergency Sobriety Card with them at all times. Such a card can be used whenever you are tempted to lapse, when you're in a high-risk situation, when you need support, and if you feel violent or abusive.

Carrying a card like this may sound like a lame idea, but trust us—many, many people find it *very* helpful.

EXERCISE 30 EXERCISE

Making Your Emergency Sobriety Card

➤ Write down the information you will put on your emergency card:

The names and phone numbers of at least five people who are part of your sober support. When you feel your sobriety is threatened, that's the time to rely on your card and call one of these people.

1. _____

2. _____

3. _____

4. _____

5. _____

➤ Three or four easy steps you can take to get yourself out of a difficult situation.

1. _____

2. _____

3. _____

4. _____

➤ A few sayings or ideas that can help you when you're tempted to lapse or that remind you why you are trying to stay sober. When you're at risk for relapse, read these out loud to yourself.

_____

_____

_____

_____

■

If you don't have supportive people you can rely on when things get rough, it's time to make new connections. Work on meeting supportive people over the next several months. Use contacts in AA or NA if necessary. Most, if not all, Twelve Step groups will give group members a phone list of all members. You can call any of these people if you need help with your recovery. This is another good reason to get involved *now* with a good support group.

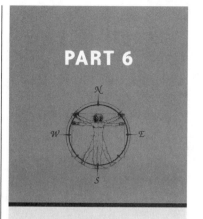

Your
Recovery Plan

You must stop drinking and using to make changes in your life. What parts of your life you need to change depends on your own situation. But a strong recovery needs a "balance" among the different parts of your life. You'll soon discover what areas you need to change. Planning those changes is your next step.

Balance Helps Maintain Sobriety

These four areas are the key to providing you with a balanced life.

1. **Continue treatment**

   Plan for continued treatment for your addiction. Support groups such as AA, NA, Men in Sobriety, or 13 Feathers are available to help you. Counseling might be another option.

2. **Physical health**

   Take care of your body. Eat good foods and learn healthy eating habits. Get regular exercise and enough rest.

3. **Recreation and leisure**

   This is a key area for any successful recovery. When you were drinking or using, most of your time was spent getting drugs, selling drugs, getting high, partying, and so on.

   Now that you are sober, you have to replace those old activities with something else. You need to find better things to do with your time. Alcohol or other drug use is not an option for you anymore. You need to find new ways of having fun doing recreational and social activities.

   Some offenders reoffend or violate probation simply because they are bored. They "miss the action" when they're straight. You *cannot* let boredom cause you to drink and use. Remember, boredom is a *choice*.

4. **Spirituality**

   Your spiritual growth can provide support for your recovery. Many people believe that only a spiritual foundation can bring true and lasting recovery.

Don't search for happiness. Search for right living . . . and happiness will be your reward.

Creating Balance

➤ **Continue treatment.** Talk with your counselor and group about your ongoing treatment. List at least three steps you can take to further support your treatment and recovery.

1. _____

2. _____

3. _____

➤ **Take care of your physical health.** Talk with your counselor and group about your physical health. List two areas you could change to improve your health.

1. _____

   _____

2. _____

   _____

List three steps you can take to begin making these changes.

1. _____

2. _____

3. _____

➤ **Plan for recreation and leisure.** Think of the most difficult times of the day and week, times when you feel like drinking or using. List them below in order from most to least difficult.

Most difficult: _____

_____

_____

_____

_____

_____

Least difficult: _____

Why is each difficult for you?

_____

_____

_____

List the people you already know who will support positive changes in your life and who already participate in positive leisure-time activities.

_____

_____

_____

List leisure activities you have enjoyed in the past (but *don't* include ones that involved drinking or using!).

_____   _____

_____   _____

_____   _____

_____   _____

List positive, healthy activities that you gave up because of your addiction.

_____   _____

_____   _____

_____   _____

List the activities you will continue to do now that you're in recovery.

_____   _____

_____   _____

_____   _____

"I never knew what 'integrity' really meant. I didn't follow any standard—I just did what I needed to do according to the needs of the moment. Then, in prison, there was the criminal code to follow, and again I did what I 'had to.'

"To change, I had to establish and follow a set of values. Something's either right or wrong; there can't be any 'in between.' Having integrity means having and living where right and wrong are clearly different. It's a simple idea, but for a long time, it wasn't easy to establish."

— Miguel,
A New Direction
program participant

Make a list of new leisure-time activities you'd like to do and have never done before.

_____   _____

_____   _____

_____   _____

_____   _____

List four reasons why it's important for your recovery and sobriety to have positive leisure-time activities.

1. _____

2. _____

3. _____

4. _____

EXERCISE **32** EXERCISE

Twenty Things I Would Like to Do

➤ Now that you've finished exercise 31, complete the following table on the next page.

Complete the table on the next page by listing some of the leisure-time activities you came up with in exercise 31. Next to each activity, answer the question listed with a **Y** for yes and an **N** for no.

20 things I like to do and/or would like to do	Does it cost money?	Is it a solo activity?	Does it require planning?	Would your parents like it?	Would your partner like it?
1					
2					
3					
4					
5					
6					
7					
8					
9					
10					
11					
12					
13					
14					
15					
16					
17					
18					
19					
20					

Spirituality

Your spiritual growth can provide support for your recovery. Many people believe that only a spiritual foundation can bring true and lasting recovery.

Right now, feeling hopeless about your addiction is normal. What do you do when your life feels out of control and unmanageable and you feel powerless? Do what millions of others have done. Believe in a power outside of and greater than yourself. Make a decision to ask for help from that higher power and from people who understand. Your higher power can have many names: Allah, God, the Great Spirit, the Tao, Yahweh, Higher Power. Your support group can also serve as your higher power.

It doesn't matter what the name is. The important thing is that you believe in this power outside yourself. You should also believe that this power is greater than yourself. A power greater than you? This may sound strange to you, but face it—you've believed in many powers greater than yourself: money, power, fame, drugs, and alcohol, to name a few. This power is so strong that it will help you overcome your addiction.

Why do people believe in a power greater than themselves? Because they have seen the changes in others before them. Ask your sponsor, group leader, or a senior peer about this. And listen to what other people say.

Addiction is a lonely illness.

As an addict, you became very isolated and mistrustful. It is hard to believe that others will help you. But if you let them try, the acceptance and support you receive will give you hope. You will realize that you don't have to do this alone. You can have hope. Your life does have meaning.

Your spiritual growth can provide support for your recovery.

Addiction and crime brought disaster to your life. You thought you were in charge of your life. But look where it landed you—behind bars. Nothing will change for the better as long as you keep trying to control yourself and others.

Try something different. Ask for help from a higher power and others who understand what it takes to make that change. If you believe that you have all the answers, you can't begin this spiritual path. Above all, you need to quit being selfish. If you don't, it will kill you.

It's time to lead a life based on spiritual principles. But to do this, you need to let go of control and take direction from a higher power and others who understand addiction.

It might seem hard to believe that something outside of you actually cares for you. Many people before you felt this way, too. But it's true. You may not always get what you want, but you will *always* get what you need.

EXERCISE **33** EXERCISE

Steps to Strengthen Your Spiritual Life

➤ Talk to your counselor and your group members (and to your sponsor, if you have one now) about spirituality. Describe at least three steps you can take to strengthen your spiritual life.

1. _____

2. _____

3. _____

Your Recovery Plan

The next exercise will help you see all the issues you'll need to include in your recovery plan. Everyone's list is different. List all of the issues that are important in your life, *even if* they don't seem to be directly linked to relapse or sobriety. For example, if you are married, relationship issues need to be in your plan.

Review the following list of issues with your group *before* you start to work on your recovery plan. You'll save time and effort that way.

EXERCISE **34** EXERCISE

Preparing to Write Your Recovery Plan

➤ **Step 1:**

The following list of issues are commonly found in recovery plans. Check the ones that apply to you.

____ career or work issues (such as transportation, drunk-driving issues)

____ money problems	____ legal problems
____ marital issues	____ relationships
____ parenting	____ family issues
____ codependency (being too dependent on others)	____ mental health functioning
____ sex or sexuality	____ leisure or fun
____ managing emotions	____ stress management
____ physical health	____ grief issues

____ nutrition   ____ assertiveness

____ spirituality   ____ self-esteem

____ abuse or victim issues   ____ anger/feelings

____ other (write in): _____

➤ **Step 2:**

After showing your list to the group and getting their feedback, write down the list of issues you will use in your recovery plan. You may include issues that were not included in the list in step 1.

_____

_____

_____

_____

_____

Writing Your Recovery Plan

Now it is time to bring together all the work you've been doing in this workbook. It's time to actually write down your recovery plan.

Writing Your Recovery Plan

Writing down your recovery plan will improve your chances of staying sober and crime free once you are out from behind bars. You should take this plan with you once you are released. It's your own personal map to your recovery. Use a notebook if you need more space for your answers.

➤ 1. **Your Recovery Goals.**

Review the goals that you listed in exercise 27. This will help you get started. Then, write down five recovery goals. These could be new recovery goals or goals you've written down before. Under each goal, write the steps you'll need to take to reach that goal.

Recovery goal #1: _____

Steps to reach this goal:

_____

_____

Recovery goal #2: _____

Steps to reach this goal:

_____

_____

Recovery goal #3: _____

Steps to reach this goal:

_____

_____

Recovery goal #4: _____

Steps to reach this goal:

_____

_____

Recovery goal #5: _____

Steps to reach this goal:

_____

_____

➤ 2. **Relapse Prevention.**

The relapse warning signs and relapse prevention plans you made for your release triggers are important. Review your answers to exercises 12 and 9.

Write down five places to stay away from.

1. _____

2. _____

3. _____

4. _____

5. _____

Write down five triggers or cravings for you.

1. _____

2. _____

3. _____

4. _____

5. _____

➤ 3. **Your Sobriety Plan.**

Review your answers to exercise 28, Your Sobriety Plan. In the space provided, write down the most important parts of your plan. Is it finding a trusted sober person to talk to? Is it finding activities to do that don't involve alcohol and other drugs? Be specific. This is *your* plan for sobriety—nobody else's. Really think about situations that might be tough for you and how you'll handle them. Be realistic.

_____

_____

_____

_____

_____

_____

_____

_____

_____

_____

_____

_____

_____

➤ 4. **Your Emergency Card.**
Review your answers to exercise 30, Making Your
Emergency Sobriety Card, and write the information
in the space provided. Also, write the information on a
piece of paper that you can carry with you at all times.
This information is that important.

_____

_____

_____

_____

_____

_____

➤ 5. **Keep in mind all the important parts of your life when making your plan.**

Review your answers to exercise 34, Preparing to Write Your Recovery Plan. What issues in step 1 do you relate to most? Write down some of the toughest issues for you to deal with (step 2 of exercise 34).

_____

_____

_____

_____

_____

Now, in the space provided, explain how you will deal with these issues.

_____

_____

_____

_____

_____

_____

➤ 6. **Show your finished plan to your support group
and therapist.**
Ask them to help you make it work better for you.
In the space provided, write down the suggestions
you were given.

_____

_____

_____

_____

_____

_____

_____

_____

_____

_____

_____

*Your recovery plan is
your own personal
map to recovery.*

REMEMBER: No plan is perfect.

You will change. Your life will change. None of us can see into the future. Your plan is a work in progress. You will need to look at and change your plan regularly. Some things that are relapse triggers for you now won't be triggers in the future. That's the good news.

The most important skill for building long-term recovery is program management. That means being able to see your program as it's working in your life and change it when you need to make it work better.

With strong program management skills, you will be able to adjust your program to whatever life throws at you—both the tough stuff *and* the good stuff.

Making a 72-Hour Plan

The first few days after your release are very important for your recovery. This will be a hard time for you, especially the first twenty-four hours. You will likely feel unsure of yourself and a bit lost. Where do you go? What will you do? Who will you see? Where will you start?

You can get through this time—*if you are prepared!* Once again, it's very important to make a plan for this time *before* you are released. You *need* to be prepared.

EXERCISE 36 EXERCISE

My 72-Hour Plan

➤ The chart on the next page is a kind of three-day (seventy-two-hour) calendar. You need to plan ahead for the first three days after your release. Your job is to fill out this chart. For each hour of each day, you need to list exactly where you'll be, what you will be doing, and who (if anyone) you will be with. Be sure to write in times for support group

MY 72-HOUR PLAN

	DAY 1	DAY 2	DAY 3
6 AM			
7 AM			
8 AM			
9 AM			
10 AM			
11 AM			
NOON			
1 PM			
2 PM			
3 PM			
4 PM			
5 PM			
6 PM			
7 PM			
8 PM			
9 PM			
10 PM			
11 PM			
MIDNIGHT			
1 AM			
2 AM			
3 AM			
4 AM			
5 AM			

meetings, contacts with your supervising agent and your sponsor, and so forth (it may help to review exercise 28, Your Sobriety Plan). Also include *daily* times for a personal inventory and reading, meditation, or prayer. You should have a balance of work (or job searches), school (if you are taking some classes), family time, leisure activity, and enough sleep. Be sure to ask your group leader or a senior peer for help if you need it.

Remember that this plan can be changed. Maybe a job interview fell through. Or maybe you were going to go jogging one morning but it rained. These things happen. If you need to make a change, put another positive activity in its place. Call your sponsor or other sober friend to talk about it. Sometimes things don't work out. For times like these, have five or six extra activities planned into your day. Your goal is to have these three days completely planned. That way you can avoid getting yourself into high-risk situations.

When you are finished with your plan, take it to your group and ask the other group members to go over it with you. They and your group leader can help you see ways to make it even better. Remember, your goal is to make a plan that will keep you away from high-risk situations and free from alcohol, drugs, and crime. The suggestions and changes your group makes are not meant as put-downs. The people in your group probably know you well and can help you see danger where you don't see it. They want you to succeed. Let them help.

Fill in the calendar on page 117 with your three-day plan for what you will do from the time you walk out the door until seventy-two hours later.

Making a One-Week Plan

After your first three days of freedom, you will feel a little more comfortable on the outside. But planning how you spend your time is still very important. Having nothing to do and being bored are powerful high-risk factors for relapse. What times of day are most difficult for you? Is it late at night—when you used to meet friends, get high, and party? Or is it in the morning when you get up—when you used to have that first joint of the day? You need to plan positive, constructive activities for times like these.

In your One-Week Plan, you don't have to account for every minute of every day like you did in the 72-Hour Plan. But you *do* need to write in what you plan to do for the week. If you look at your plan and see three or four spots where you have nothing going for three, four, or five hours at a time, that could mean trouble. A spur-of-the-moment idea for something to do just might be a poor choice.

Again, pay extra attention to the times of day you know are difficult for you, and be sure you have something positive planned. Remember, too, that just because you have something planned at a certain time doesn't mean you can't change it. Maybe you'd planned to go to a gym to work out on Saturday afternoon. But that morning, a (sober) friend calls you and invites you to go with him and his kids to a baseball game. If you want to go, that's fine. The purpose of making a plan is simply to be sure you aren't sitting around with nothing to do—except to think about using, drinking, or committing crime.

Remember, too, that just because you have something planned at a certain time doesn't mean you can't change it.

Planning how you spend your time is very important.

Sometimes, things you scheduled don't work out. Have five or six extra activities planned into your day, just in case this happens. In other words, it's okay to overplan your days a little. Again, your goal is to avoid boredom and times when you've got nothing good to do. These are the times when you would be most tempted to drink, use, or get into criminal activity.

Make these plans each week until you feel more comfortable dealing with life on the outside. Go over each week's plan with your sponsor and support group. They will be able to help you with activities and spot any potential risk areas, too.

EXERCISE 37 EXERCISE

Making a One-Week Plan

➤ Use the chart on the next page to make your One-Week Plan. In each block of time, write down what you're going to do, when it will start, and when it will end.

When you're finished, show your plan to your sponsor and support group. Ask them to help you make it work better for you.

➤ Sponsor/support group suggestions:

_____

_____

_____

_____

_____

MY ONE-WEEK PLAN

	DAY 1	DAY 2	DAY 3	DAY 4	DAY 5	DAY 6	DAY 7
MORNING							
AFTERNOON							
EVENING / NIGHT							

Foresight vs. Hindsight

Thinking ahead, planning, anticipating problems and avoiding them—that's *foresight*. Thinking after you act is *hindsight*. Don't wait until you're in the middle of a problem when your only choice is to react. Look closely at this list. Where do you usually fit?

FORESIGHT: *Thinking **before** You Act*	**HINDSIGHT:** *Thinking **after** You Act*
1. Plan ahead.	1. No matter what, I must get my own way.
2. Anticipate. Ask, what? How?	2. It's not necessary to talk about my intentions with anyone.
3. Be open to learning from other healthy people.	3. I'm not open to listening or learning from others.
4. Look for the facts and do not rely on assumptions.	4. Make decisions based only on assumptions and feelings.
5. Express thoughts and feelings in the least threatening way.	5. Rely on feelings of the moment rather than rational thinking.
6. Practice total honesty with my higher power, counselor, partner, agent, boss, close friends, sober support group, and sponsor.	6. Avoid hurt and disappointment at all costs.
7. Let go of power and control over others.	7. Hang on to power and control over others.

Thinking Ahead:
A Daily Relapse Prevention Inventory

Answer the following questions. By doing so, you'll be writing your own plan to avoid relapse.

➤ What clues were there today that you were building up to drinking, using drugs, or criminal behavior?

_____

_____

_____

➤ What high-risk situations today could trigger a relapse for you?

_____

_____

_____

➤ What's your plan for avoiding relapse?

_____

_____

_____

_____

Making a Crisis Plan

It is now time to make a crisis plan. At some point, you will be in the middle of a life crisis. It could be a serious illness or the death of someone very close to you, an accident, the loss of your job, or your partner leaving.

When such a crisis happens, your whole daily schedule is disrupted. You may be tempted to tell yourself that you don't have time to go to your support group meetings, to do your daily recovery disciplines, to get exercise, and so on. You may also be tempted to give up recovery altogether. Don't take this road. You can live through a crisis and still maintain your recovery! In fact, it's more important than ever that you focus on your recovery during a crisis. Will you be able to do all your usual recovery activities on your calendar? Probably not. But you *can* still take care of yourself.

EXERCISE 39 EXERCISE

Making a Crisis Plan

➤ Think about how you will take care of yourself when you are stressed out because of a crisis. Then, include the following areas in your crisis plan. You may choose to write your plan in your notebook.

1. Don't panic and give up. Sit down and make a plan.

2. Contact your sponsor and tell him what's happening. Also, AA has a crisis intervention hotline you can call at any time (see page 145).

3. Tell your support group what's happening. If you need to be out of town, they can help you get phone numbers of support groups all across the country and Canada.

Some hospitals have regular AA meetings. You *can* find other support group meetings. When you go, tell everyone what's happening to you and ask for help. You'll receive it!

4. Figure out ways to get some exercise even during a crisis. List ideas here:

_____

_____

_____

_____

5. Figure out healthy ways to relieve the extra stress you'll be under. List ideas here:

_____

_____

_____

_____

You can live through a crisis and still maintain your recovery!

6. Recall past crisis times. Did you relapse? If so, what are the warning signs of relapse?

_____

_____

_____

_____

"Four weeks ago, a friend of mine cut his throat with a razor blade. He lived. Last night, a friend of mine hung himself in his cell. He died. Am I going to end up like them? Are you? I used to wonder about it. I even swallowed three razor blades back in 1987. I was so tired of life. I'm thirty-five years old and I am in prison for the fifth time. Drugs and drinking are my downfall. 100 percent. No more for me. Easy to say, but hard to do, right? AA can show us a lot if we listen. AA and treatment have given me a way out of drugs and drinking and have given me hope for the future. The more I listen, the more help I get. Like they say, 'The program works if you work it.'"

— David H.,
  aggravated burglary, 20 years,
  Branchville Training Center,
  Indiana
  (Free at Last)

7. Figure out what parts of your plan you *can* adapt and keep in place during the crisis—even if you're away from home, living at a hospital, and so on. List ideas here:

_____

_____

_____

_____

8. What other issues do you think you will need to plan for?

_____

_____

_____

_____

_____

_____

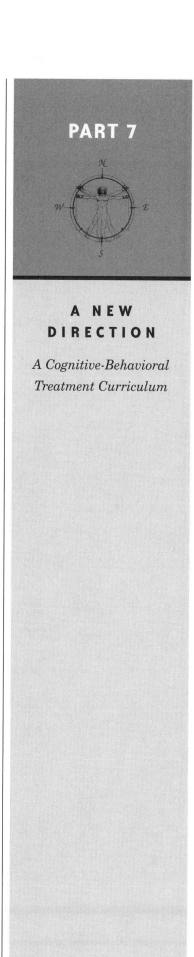
Progress, Not Perfection

You can be very proud of the efforts you've made so far in your recovery from drinking or using. You'll notice the benefits of sobriety when you start seeing the positive changes in your life.

Relapse Recovery Quiz

Are you recovery bound or relapse bound? This exercise will help you find out. *Recovery bound* means you are on track to stay in recovery. *Relapse bound* shows you're at risk for relapse. A low score under Recovery Bound is common during the early stages of recovery.

On the line before each item, rate the behavior on a scale of 1 to 5. A 1 means you can't relate to the behavior and 5 means you can totally relate to it. Read each item carefully.

➤ **Recovery Bound** (Rate 1 to 5)

____ being honest, realistic about self and problems

____ socializing with others

____ listening, accepting input from others

____ asking for help. Accepting help

____ having a positive attitude

____ focusing on personal recovery

____ trusting, sharing with others

____ having harmonious relationships

____ turning your will over to a higher power

____ having a stable lifestyle

____ taking responsibility for your own behavior

____ being warm, friendly, caring about others

____ accepting of the future

____ sharing

____ being emotionally stable

____ appreciating what you have

____ being open, outgoing

____ finding purpose in day-to-day life

____ getting the job done

____ forgiving and understanding

____ being assertive

____ being truthful with yourself

____ being content with what you have

____ trusting

____ being open-minded

____ being willing to admit faults

____ cooperating

____ attending support group meetings

____ having a close working relationship with your sponsor

____ having reasonable expectations

____ sharing thoughts and feelings openly

____ being considerate, showing humility

____ having an attitude of gratitude for the blessings of life

____ acting mature

____ actively working the steps of recovery

____ fully accepting the need for abstinence

____ understanding the disease concept of addiction

____ sharing your recovery

____ openly sharing with others about your experience with the disease of addiction

___ appearing peaceful, comfortable with self

___ taking responsibility for solutions

___ acting cheerful, outgoing

___ actively being helpful and supportive

___ discussing spiritual aspects of recovery

➤ **Relapse Bound** (Rate 1 to 5)

___ minimizing, maximizing, distorting, lying, using excuses

___ avoiding others, isolating yourself

___ not listening, acting like you know it all

___ not asking for help

___ having a negative attitude

___ focusing on too many concerns outside recovery

___ being suspicious, distrustful

___ having conflict with others

___ depending on personal willpower

___ having an unstable lifestyle

___ blaming, being resentful, feeling "victimized"

___ being hostile, taking advantage of others

___ worrying about and fearing the future

___ being selfish

___ being emotionally out of control

___ being ungrateful and obsessed with your own problems

___ keeping to yourself, being withdrawn

___ feeling aimless, having no direction

___ stalling

____ being resentful

____ being passive

____ being dishonest with yourself

____ envying things others have

____ being paranoid

____ having tunnel vision, being closed to new ideas and help

____ being self-righteous

____ dominating

____ not attending support group meetings often

____ seldom, if ever, seeing your sponsor

____ being demanding of yourself and others

____ not being open, acting phony

____ being arrogant, self-centered

____ pitying yourself, focusing on what's missing

____ acting immature

____ not working the steps of recovery

____ refusing to accept the need for abstinence

____ rejecting the disease concept

____ hiding, being unwilling to discuss the recovery process

____ hiding your addiction from others

____ appearing angry, agitated

____ looking for "magic" solutions to problems

____ acting depressed, withdrawn

____ unwilling to be helpful, supportive to others

____ showing no evidence of spiritual growth

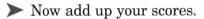

➤ Now add up your scores.

 Recovery Bound Score: _____

 Relapse Bound Score: _____

➤ After completing this exercise, review your scores with
your sponsor, counselor, or support group. The goal is to
have a higher score in the Recovery Bound section than
the Relapse Bound section. Ask others to comment on your
scores. Take this quiz each week. It can quickly show you
what areas you need to work on most. Keep in mind that
each time you take this quiz, your score will be different
depending on what recovery stage you are in.

What to Do If Relapse Happens

Relapse is a possibility. Obsessing about it is not useful. But you should have a plan for relapse. Knowing what to do and being prepared is the key to recovery.

If you start using alcohol or other drugs again, the first thing to do is to stop immediately. You may feel like saying, "Well, I screwed up now, so I might as well just go all the way. Get really ripped. What's the point? I failed."

DON'T LET THAT HAPPEN. Stop that kind of thinking as soon as it starts. Yes, you'll feel guilty and disappointed in yourself after using or drinking again. But it's very important not to give in and tell yourself it's okay to continue using or drinking.

A poor decision was made, but you can minimize the consequences by stopping immediately. Get back on the sobriety track. Immediately talk with a concerned sober person such as your sponsor, counselor, family member, friend, or clergy person about it, someone who can help you return to working your recovery plan. You may also need more help—professional help. You may even need to enter a treatment program again.

All of this is okay. The first step for you is to stop drinking and using and reach out for help.

■

You may think of recovery as a difficult and endless task. It's time to change your thinking. It's time to think in a new way about these changes. If you think of recovery as a burden, like going on a diet, it just won't work.

View it as a truly remarkable adventure, because that is exactly what it is. Accept the support others are offering to you. Your new life will offer you so much that you won't want to give it up.

And your life *will* change. By showing up, staying sober, and working on your recovery program, you'll eventually have financial security, your urges and cravings will leave you, your relationships will improve, and you'll have love in your life. These things happen because of your recovery program. You don't have to plan to make them happen.

Remember, too, that there aren't huge immediate payoffs. It is addictive thinking to expect immediate results: "I was good today, so what do I get in return?" These positive changes do take time. But they do come.

After a while, staying in balance will no longer seem like something you *have* to do, but something you *want* to do. You will begin to truly like the new person you've become. This new caring for yourself and the pride it creates will build new feelings of self-confidence and self-esteem. This is a hope-filled process.

Even if you are not yet at the point where you have started to feel this way, it's important that you know this place exists. By doing the work involved, you can get there. This is not a fantasy or an illusion or a trick or a con. You *can* reach a point where you *want* to be in recovery—a point where your passion for recovery is as strong as your passion for drinking, using, and crime once was.

The information, suggestions, and guidelines we've provided can help you start on the road to recovery. You *can* recover. You *can* create better relationships and live a richer, more fulfilling life. Reach out to others for strength, support, and encouragement. Everything that you *need* will be given to you.

Resources

AA Temporary Sponsorship Program: A Gateway from Correctional Facilities to Alcoholics Anonymous.
For more information, contact Minneapolis Intergroup, 6300 Walker St., St. Louis Park, MN 55416. (952) 922-0880.

Books on Healthy Sexuality

Betcher, William. *Intimate Play: Creating Romance in Everyday Life.* New York: Penguin, 1988.

Geringer Woititz, Janet. *The Intimacy Struggle.* Deerfield Beach, Fla.: Health Communications, 1993.

Godek, Gregory J. P. *1001 Ways to Be Romantic.* Naperville, Ill.: Sourcebooks, 1999.

Schnarch, David. *Passionate Marriage: Love, Sex, and Intimacy in Emotionally Committed Relationships.* New York: Holt, 1998.

Sources

Bachom, Sandi, and Don Ross. *Denial Is Not a River in Egypt.* Center City, Minn.: Hazelden, 1998.

Daley, Dennis C., Howard B. Moss, and Frances Campbell. *Dual Disorders: Counseling Clients with Chemical Dependency and Mental Illness.* 2d ed. Center City, Minn.: Hazelden, 1993.

Hermes, Sheila. *Assertiveness: Practical Skills for Positive Communication.* Center City, Minn.: Hazelden, 1998.

Mambuca, Annette, ed. *Free at Last: Daily Meditations by and for Inmates.* Center City, Minn.: Hazelden, 1993.

Minnesota Department of Corrections. *Triad Relapse/Reoffense Prevention Workbook.* St. Paul: Minnesota State Department of Corrections, 1996.

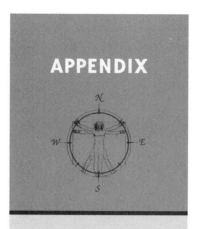

APPENDIX

A NEW DIRECTION

A Cognitive-Behavioral Treatment Curriculum

The Twelve Steps
of Alcoholics Anonymous

1. We admitted we were powerless over alcohol—that our lives had become unmanageable.

2. Came to believe that a Power greater than ourselves could restore us to sanity.

3. Made a decision to turn our will and our lives over to the care of God *as we understood Him.*

4. Made a searching and fearless moral inventory of ourselves.

5. Admitted to God, to ourselves, and to another human being the exact nature of our wrongs.

6. Were entirely ready to have God remove all these defects of character.

7. Humbly asked Him to remove our shortcomings.

8. Made a list of all persons we had harmed, and became willing to make amends to them all.

9. Made direct amends to such people wherever possible, except when to do so would injure them or others.

10. Continued to take personal inventory and when we were wrong promptly admitted it.

11. Sought through prayer and meditation to improve our conscious contact with God *as we understood Him,* praying only for knowledge of His will for us and the power to carry that out.

12. Having had a spiritual awakening as the result of these steps, we tried to carry this message to alcoholics, and to practice these principles in all our affairs.

The Twelve Steps of AA are taken from *Alcoholics Anonymous,* 3d ed., published by AA World Services, Inc., New York, N.Y., 59–60. Reprinted with permission of AA World Services, Inc. (See editor's note on page 146.)

The Twelve Steps
of Narcotics Anonymous

1. We admitted we were powerless over our addiction, that our lives had become unmanageable.

2. We came to believe that a Power greater than ourselves could restore us to sanity.

3. We made a decision to turn our will and our lives over to the care of God *as we understood Him.*

4. We made a searching and fearless moral inventory of ourselves.

5. We admitted to God, to ourselves, and to another human being the exact nature of our wrongs.

6. We were entirely ready to have God remove all these defects of character.

7. We humbly asked Him to remove our shortcomings.

8. We made a list of all persons we had harmed, and became willing to make amends to them all.

9. We made direct amends to such people wherever possible, except when to do so would injure them or others.

10. We continued to take personal inventory and when we were wrong promptly admitted it.

11. We sought through prayer and meditation to improve our conscious contact with God *as we understood Him,* praying only for knowledge of His will for us and the power to carry that out.

12. Having had a spiritual awakening as a result of these steps, we tried to carry this message to addicts, and to practice these principles in all our affairs.

137

The Twelve-Step Alternative

1. We accept the fact that our efforts to stop using mood-altering chemicals have failed.

2. We believe that we must turn elsewhere for help.

3. We turn to our fellow men and women, particularly those who have struggled with the same problem.

4. We have made a list of the situations in which we are most likely to use mood-altering chemicals.

5. We ask our friends to help us avoid those situations.

6. We are ready to accept the help they give us.

7. We earnestly hope that they will help.

8. We have made a list of the persons we have harmed, and to whom we hope to make amends.

9. We shall do all we can to make amends, in any way that will not cause further harm.

10. We will continue to make such lists, and revise them as needed.

11. We appreciate what our friends have done, and are doing to help us.

12. We in turn are ready to help others who may come to us in the same way.

13 Feathers

Feather 1 I am a Native American. I am a Human Being. I chose not to follow the directions given by my heart of my spirit, therefore I am now chemically dependent.

Feather 2 I realize I must go back to the circle of my people, to learn the beating of our Drum and to ask the Great Spirit to restore my oneness with that circle of my people and culture, that I may one day walk once more with dignity among my people. Oh Great Spirit, hear my Drum.

Feather 3 I realize I my Drum who I am and that I must look within to find that powerful person to solve all of my problems.

Feather 4 I will search like a warrior to find my center, both fearlessly and courageously.

Feather 5 Grandfather, I stand before you. I have wronged my people, my family, and our traditions. Take pity upon me, Great Spirit.

Feather 6 Great Spirit, I come before you in a humble way. You know what is written in my heart. Help me.

Feather 7 Great Spirit, I ask you to have mercy and pity and give me the strength to fight my own greatest enemy, myself.

Feather 8 Great Spirit, I have disgraced myself and have wronged my family, my people, and our proud traditions. Oh, Great Spirit, I stand humbly before you with open arms. Great Spirit, hear me.

APPENDIX

Feather 9   Great Spirit take pity upon me and grant me the strength that I will need to confess to my family that I have brought disgrace upon them.

Feather 10   Great Spirit Grandfather, I ask that you grant me the wisdom and the courage that I will need to keep on learning more about myself and to keep on fighting myself, that I may overcome this Chemical Dependency.

Feather 11   Oh Great Spirit, I stand in this circle of life. I am struggling here on Mother Earth. Hear my heart and grant that I may come to know myself, so that I may be a human being again among my people. Hear my heart, Grandfather.

Feather 12   I must return to our traditions, the Sacred Pipe, the sweat lodge, the drum and our people that I may once again walk among these with dignity and pride and that I may once again walk the Red Road. Hear me, Grandfather. I have found my inner arrows.

Feather 13   Before I am released from this Iron House, I will attend the Sacred Sweat Lodge and sweat my last day within this Iron House. When I come out of the Sacred Sweat Lodge, I will claim back my spirit and say, "COME, LET'S GO HOME!!!"

SOS

SOS is a non-profit network of autonomous, non-professional local groups dedicated solely to helping individuals achieve and maintain sobriety. There are groups meeting regularly in many cities throughout the United States.

Guidelines for sobriety:

1. To break the cycle of denial and achieve sobriety, we first acknowledge that we are alcoholics or addicts.

2. We reaffirm this truth daily and accept without reservation the fact that as clean and sober individuals, we cannot and do not drink or use, no matter what.

3. Since drinking or using is not an option for us, we take whatever steps are necessary to continue our Sobriety Priority lifelong.

4. A quality of life, "the good life," can be achieved. However, life is also filled with uncertainties. Therefore, we do not drink or use regardless of feelings, circumstances, or conflicts.

5. We share in confidence with each other our thoughts and feelings as sober, clean individuals.

6. Sobriety is our Priority, and we are each responsible for our lives and sobriety.

Reprinted with permission from Secular Organizations for Sobriety/Save Our Selves (SOS).

APPENDIX

The Indian Twelve Steps
Walking the Red Road

1. We admitted we were powerless over alcohol—that we had lost control over our lives.

2. We came to believe that a Power greater than ourselves could help us regain control.

3. Made a decision to ask for help from a higher power and others who understand.

4. We stopped and thought about our strengths and our weaknesses and thought about ourselves.

5. We admitted to the Great Spirit, to ourselves, and to another person the things we thought were wrong about ourselves.

6. We are ready, with the help of the Great Spirit, to change.

7. We humbly asked a higher power and our friends to help us change.

8. We made a list of people who were hurt by our drinking and want to make up for these hurts.

9. We are making up to those people whenever we can, except when to do so would hurt them more.

10. We continue to think about our strengths and weaknesses and when we are wrong, we say so.

11. We pray and think about ourselves, praying only for strength to do what is right.

12. We try to help other alcoholics and to practice these principles in everything we do.

The Twelve Steps of Alcoholics Anonymous Adapted for Sexual Addicts

1. We admitted we were powerless over our sexual addiction—that our lives had become unmanageable.

2. Came to believe a Power greater than ourselves could restore us to sanity.

3. Made a decision to turn our will and our lives over to the care of God, as we understood Him.

4. Made a searching and fearless moral inventory of ourselves.

5. Admitted to God, to ourselves, and to another human being the exact nature of our wrongs.

6. Were entirely ready to have God remove all these defects of character.

7. Humbly asked Him to remove our shortcomings.

8. Made a list of all persons we had harmed, and became willing to make amends to them all.

9. Made direct amends to such people wherever possible, except when to do so would injure them or others.

10. Continued to take personal inventory and when we were wrong promptly admitted it.

11. Sought through prayer and meditation to improve our conscious contact with God as we understood Him, praying only for knowledge of His will for us and the power to carry that out.

12. Having had a spiritual awakening as the result of these steps, we tried to carry this message to others and to practice these principles in all our affairs.

SMART Recovery®
Self Management and Recovery Training

SMART Recovery® is an abstinence-based, not-for-profit organization with a self-help program for people having problems with any type of addictive behavior. SMART Recovery® teaches commonsense self-help procedures designed to empower people to abstain and to develop a more positive lifestyle.

SMART Recovery®: Purposes and methods

1. We help individuals gain independence from addictive behavior.

2. We teach how to

   - enhance and maintain motivation to abstain
   - cope with urges
   - manage thoughts, feelings, and behavior
   - balance momentary and enduring satisfactions

3. Our efforts are based on scientific knowledge, and evolve as scientific knowledge evolves.

4. Individuals who have gained independence from addictive behavior are invited to stay involved with us, to enhance their gains and help others.

Reprinted with permission from SMART Recovery®